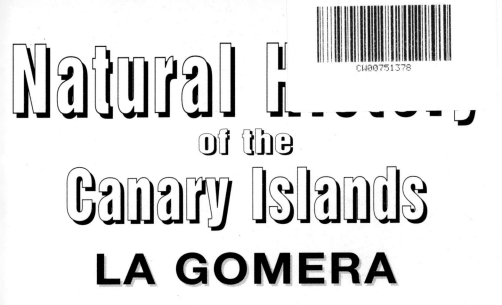

Natural History
of the
Canary Islands
LA GOMERA

POCKET GUIDE

David Bramwell
Juan Manuel López Ramírez

Editorial Rueda, S.L.

Porto Cristo, 13
28924 Alcorcón (Madrid-España)
Tels.: 91 619 27 79 - 91 619 25 64 Fax.: 91 610 28 55
www.editorialrueda,es - E-mail:ed_rueda@infornet.es

CREDITS

Illustrations:

Zoë Bramwell
Pilar Echeverria Echeveste

Photographs:

David Bramwell
José Naranjo Suárez
Juan Manuel López Ramírez

ISBN: 84-7207-119-7
ISBN: 84-7207-115-4 (Complete work)

DEPOSITO LEGAL: M-24524-1999

ACKNOWLEDGMENTS

To our colleague and friend José Carrillo Molina of the Canarian Marine Science Institute on Gran Canaria, for his invaluable help in revising the sections on marine fauna.

To our colleague and friend José Naranjo Suárez of the Viera y Clavijo Botanical Garden on Gran Canaria for the digitalization of several photographs.

To our wives Pilar and Gaby for their patience during the many afternoons and weekends taken up in preparing this guide.

To Rafael Rueda, editor of this new series for believing in this project which has now become a reality.

And finally to all those who through their constructive criticism have helped us to achieve our objective.

To our children
Alex, Vicky, Dany, Laura y Elena

...vi olmos y buxos, balos y sabinas,
viñáticos, palmas, cipreses, laureles,
vi plátanos, cedros y linaloeles,
vi assaz marmulanos, pimientas muy finas,
...
vi dragos, perfectos muy medicinales,
también leña santa para medicinas.

Octavas de Vasco Díaz Tanco de Frenegal escritor español del Siglo XVI, dedicadas a la Isla de La Gomera y recogidas en el libro *"DE LAS DOS ORILLAS"* (1989) del Dr. Alfonso Armas Ayala (1924-1998).

Sambucus palmensis   (Canary Elder)

A Canary Islands endemic in danger of extinction.
Present in the Garajony National Park.

PREFACE

The publication of a book of these characteristics which so well presents the flora and fauna of our Island, was something required by the inhabitants, students and institutions of the Island. The Cabildo Insular de la Gomera, which is aware of the high value and importance of the work carried out by David Bramwell and Juan Manuel López as well as by the rest of the team of people who have accompanied them in the elaboration of this publication, is very proud to participate with this prologue in the present edition of «Natural History of the Canary Islands: La Gomera».

La Gomera, which, with its Garajonay National Park, declared a World Heritage Site by UNESCO, has always provided an example for the conservation of natural areas for the world, can now count on this important document which will certainly help to continue the study of the Island and consequently improve its special protection.

I would like sincerely like to thank the authors for this work and also all the team who have participated in the research, edition and definitive preparation of the book, and wish to transmit to them the propensity of this Institution to help all those who wish to advance the study of the flora and fauna which complete, jointly with is orography, the imposing landscape of the Island.

Casimiro Curbelo Curbelo
PRESIDENTE DEL EXCMO. CABILDO INSULAR DE LA GOMERA

INTRODUCTION

This small pocket guide is the first of a series of seven, the same number as the islands which make up the Canarian Archipelago.

We have not tried to produce a book directed at experts on the subject, nor have we included here all the species present on La Gomera, only the most frequent and easily found. If we can help, with this book, the ordinary person, both from the islands and visiting us, to know and understand a little bit more about our environemt and natural resources we will be satisfied.

The high proportion of endemic species which are only found on the islands and in no other part of the world makes them extemely important both as a natural resource and from a scientific point of view. To lose these species through extinction is to lose a valuable natural heritage and signifies the deterioration of the quality of insular life not only for the present inhabitants but also for future generations.

The authors

CONTENTS

PROTECTED NATURAL AREAS

LOCALITIES

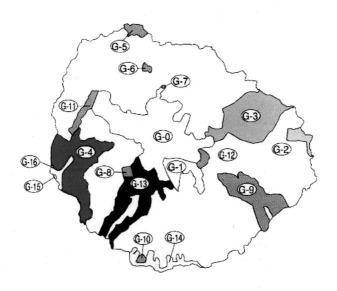

G-0   GARAJONAY NATIONAL PARK

G-1   BENCHIJIGUA INTEGRAL NATURE RESERVE

G-2   PUNTALLANA SPECIAL NATURE RESERVE

G-3   MAJONA NATURAL PARK

G-4   VALLE GRAN REY RURAL PARK

G-5   LOS ORGANOS NATURAL MONUMENT

G-6   ROQUE CANO NATURAL MONUMENT

G-7   ROQUE BLANCO NATURAL MONUMENT

G-8   LA FORTALEZA NATURAL MONUMENT

G-9   BARRANCO DEL CABRITO NATURAL MONUMENT

G-10 LA CALDERA NATURAL MONUMENT

G-11 LOMO DEL CARRETON NATURAL MONUMENT

G-12 LOS ROQUES NATURAL MONUMENT

G-13 ORONE PROTECTED LANDSCAPE

G-14 ALAJERO CLIFFS SITE OF SCIENTIFIC INTEREST

G-15 CHARCO DEL CONDE SITE OF SCIENTIFIC INTEREST

G-16 CHARCO DEL CIENO SITE OF SCIENTIFIC INTEREST

LA GOMERA

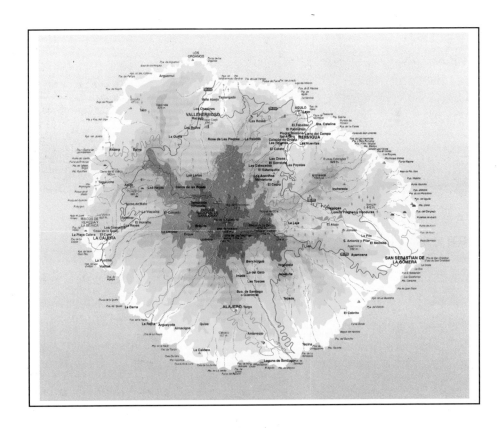

PLACES OF INTEREST

PLACES OF INTEREST

The island of La Gomera reaches about 1450 m. in the centre, and the slopes of its dome-like summit are dissected into 38 deep radial barrancos which open up towards the coast between steep cliffs. The south of the island is warm and dry without a wide coastal plain and the north is steep, reminiscent of the north coast of Tenerife.

The most interesting places for seeing something of the natural history are: the Barranco de la Villa, Roque de Agando, Riscos de Agulo, Roque Cano, Bosque de El Cedro, Chorros de Epina, Arure, Valle Gran Rey, Barranco de Argaga and Chipude.

BARRANCO DE LA VILLA

The largest ravine on the island extends from the centre to the East coast where the capital of the island , San Sebastian de La Gomera, nestles in the mouth of the valley.

On the north side the main road which links the capital to Hermigua and Vallehermoso passes close to the high cliffs. On these cliffs numerous endemic plants can be found. *Sideritis gomeraea* with woolly leaves and pendulous inflorescences is abundant whilst a second species *Sideritis lotsyi* is rather rarer. *Dicheranthus plocamoides* which also occurs in the Teno

PLACES OF INTEREST

mountains of Tenerife, is frequent on the rocks along with the solitary rosettes of *Greenovia diplocycla*. On the dry slopes the small flowered *Argyranthemum frutescens* mingles with *Senecio kleinia* and several species of *Euphorbia*. Amongst the dry rocks at least four species of the genus *Aeonium occur, A. subplanum* with flat, green rosettes, *A. decorum* with reddish leaves and two glaucous, greyish-leaved species *A. castello-paivae* and *A. gomerense*. In the nearby Barranco de la Laja another, rare, species of Aeonium can be found, *A. saundersii*. In Spring the rocks and cliffs tend to be covered with the golden flowers of the Gomeran endemic *Lotus emeroides*.

ROQUE DE AGANDO

This basaltic monolith situated in the high part of the Barranco de la Laja is best aproached from Tagamiche and the road from San Sebastian to the south. The path passes through an area of Brezal *(Erica arborea)* and drops towards the base of the Tagamiche cliffs where three

local endemics can be found, *Echium acanthocarpum* a tall shrub with blue flowers, *Argyranthemum callichrysum* a daisy with attractive yellow flowers and *Crambe gomeraea*. At the base of the Agando rock there

there are large colonies of *Aeonium rubrolineatum* with pinkish-yellow flowers and a rare species of *Sideritis* resembling *S. marmorea*. The humid rocky zones house colonies of the orchid *Neotinea intacta* and two yellow-flowered shrubs are common, *Adenocarpus foliolosus* with sticky narrow leaves and *Teline stenopetala* in one of its many variable forms, on this occasion with small, oblong leaves. If walking there is a good path which returns to San Sebastian via the Barranco de la Laja.

RISCOS DE AGULO, ROQUE CANO.

These two areas of basalt cliffs are considered together as they have similar floras. The Agulo cliffs house two endemic species of the genus *Sonchus, S. gonzalez-padronii*, which is quite common on the cliffs towards the West of the island and *S. regis-jubae* which appears to be limited to the North between Agulo and Vallehermoso. On the other hand the rare *Silene bougaei and Limonium brassicifolium* appear to be more or less confined to the Agulo area.

Roque Cano, in the Vallehermoso valley has perpendicular faces. The  slopes below the rock are covered by shrubs of *Juniperus canariensis* (sabina) and for the curious endemic grass *Brachypodium arbuscula*. The southern faces of Roque Cano have several interesting species, of plants, *Sonchus ortunoi*, *Senecio hermosae* (a local endemic) *Dicheranthus*

PLACES OF INTEREST

plocamoides, and *Aeonium viscatum,* a small, sticky plant. On the slopes of the northern side there are shrubs such as *Teline gomerae* with large leaves, *Sonchus regis-jubae* and the blue-flowered *Globularia salicina.*

BOSQUES DE EL CEDRO

In the central region of La Gomera, one of the best forests of laurisilva is found. It was designated a World Heritage Site by UNESCO in 1986 and forms the nucleus of the Garajonay National Park.

The forests of El Cedro in the highest parts of the Hermigua valley are the richest of all. The dominant trees are *Laurus azorica* (laurel), *Ilex canariensis* (holly), *Myrica faya* (wax-myrtle) and *Salix canariensis* (Canary willow). The shrub layer is formed of species such as *Hypericum grandifolium, Cedronella canariensis, Gesnouinia arborea, Scrophularia smithii ssp. langaeana, Teline stenopetala, and Bystropogon canariensis.* The ferns *Woodwardia radicans, Athyrium umbrosum* and *Asplenium onopteris* are abundant along the edges of the many streams.

Some of the species occurring in the National Park are considered to be close to extinction, these include *Euphorbia mellifera, Pericallis hansenii* and *Sambucus palmensis.*

PLACES OF INTEREST

With respect to the fauna, the best represented groups in the laurel forests and fayal-brezal woodlands are the insects and molluscs amongst the invertebrates, and the birds amongst the vertebrates.

In the leaf-litter on the ground coleopteran beetles of the Carabid group are most abundant, many of the species being endemic. Amongst the Lepidoptera the cleopatra butterfly (*Gonepterix cleobule*), also endemic to the islands, is most notable.

The birds are well represented in this type of forest by the local blackbird (*Turdus merula cabrerae*) , the common chaffinch (*Fringilla coelebs tintillon*), the robin or redbreast (*Erithacus rubecula superbus*), the goldcrest (*Regulus regulus teneriffae*) etc. However, the two most emblematic species are representatives of the Columbidae family, Bolle's laurel pigeon (*Columba bollii*) and the white-tailed laurel pigeon (*Columba junoniae*) both endemic to the Canary Islands.

The forests of El Cedro are easily accessible from San Sebastian or from Hermigua.

CHORROS DE EPINA, ARURE

The north coast road from Vallehermoso continues towards Valle Gran Rey across the western slopes of the island. After about a 30 minute car

PLACES OF INTEREST

journey there is a small track which leads to a spring known as the Chorros de Epina. At the edge of this path the shrub *Gesnouinia arborea* and the tree-heath *Erica scoparia* can be found. Near the stream and on the cliffs above the very rare spurge (*Euphorbia lambii*) can be encountered with its large yellow bracts surrounding the flowers.

Climbing up towards the base of the cliffs which go on towards the west several very rare plant species can be seen including *Sideritis nutans, Pimpinella junionae* and *Sonchus gonzalez-padronii* amongst others.

Returning to the Valle Gran Rey road, which winds towards the village of Arure, this passes through a woodland area where *Geranium canariense, Hedera canariensis* and *Andryala pinnatifida* abound.

VALLE GRAN REY, BARRANCO DE ARGAGA, CHIPUDE

The southwest zone of the Island of La Gomera with its deep valleys and high cliffs is rich in endemic plants which are often quite difficult to find. The great ravine of Valle Gran Rey has high cliffs which are almost inaccesible and to a consideable extent, unexplored.

On the cliffs at the side of the road several species are common,  *Descurainia millefolia,* a large form of *Aeonium decorum* with intensely red leaves, *Sonchus filifolius* with small yellow flowers and, in some places *Sideritis nutans* with strongly smelling leaves.

In the bed of the valley there are extensive palm groves and groups of tamarisk. To the south of Valle Gran Rey, the Barranco of Argaga is found. In the lower, dry part of this ravine there are populations of *Echium triste* and the almost extinct shrub, *Limonium dendroides.*

Further to the south the village of Chipude is domi-nated by a large flat-topped mountain known as the Fortaleza. Here several of the Island's most interes-ting endemic plants can be found. We recommend a visit to this locality. The local traditional life has changed little and it is still possible to buy articles of pottery made in the same way as that of the original inhabitants of the island many centuries ago. The  cliffs of the Fortaleza are rich in endemic plants such as *Sideritis lotsyi, Aeonium urbicum, Pimpinella junionae, Ceropegia ceratophora, Limonium redivivum* and *Crambe gomeraea* amongst many others.

FLORA

Tortula muralis   Hedw

FAMILY: Pottiaceae
HABITAT: common on rocks, walls, tree trunks, etc. Found between 50 and 1.600 m.
COMMENTS: present on all the islands

Thamniom alopecurum   (Hedw.) B.S.G.

FAMILY: Neckeraceae
HABITAT: humid, shady sites, on tree trunks and the ground.
COMMENTS: found only on the central and western Canary Islands.

Polytrichum juniperinum   (Willd.) Hedw.

FAMILY: Polytrichaceae.
HABITAT: dry forest soils, especially the fayal-brezal (500 to 1.600 m.).
COMMENTS: found only on the central and western Canary Islands.

Philonotis fontana   (Hedw.) Brid.

FAMILY: Bartramiaceae
**HABITAT: between dry rocks up to
500 m.**
**COMMENTS: recorded only on La
Gomera and Tenerife.**

Mnium undulatum   (Weis) Hedw.

FAMILY: Mniaceae
**HABITAT: humid sites; barranco and
aqueduct borders, the darkest forests,
between 500 and 1.200 m.**
**COMMENTS: central and western
Canaries only.**

Isothecium myosutoides   Brid.

FAMILY: Hypnaceae
**HABITAT: rocks and trees in humid
areas of the Laurisilvia. (800 to 1.200
m.)**
**COMMENTS: central and western
Canaries only.**

BRYOPHYTES - MOSSES

Funaria hygrometrica Hedw.

FAMILY: Funariaceae
HABITAT: open sunny sites of the laurel forests, where it is common, and shaded sites of the low zone (400 to 1.000 m.)
COMMENTS: present on all the islands.

Fissidens taxifolius Hedw.

FAMILY: Fissidentaceae
HABITAT: humid shaded sites in the Laurisilva.
COMMENTS: Tenerife and La Gomera only.

Cinclidotus mucronatus (Brid.) Mach.

FAMILY: Pottiaceae
HABITAT: damp rocks and the lower borders of the forests.
COMMENTS: a Mediterranean/ Atlantic species found only on La Gomera.

FLORA - CRYPTOGAMS

BRYOPHYTES - MOSSES

Bryum capillare (L.) Hedw.

FAMILY: Bryaceae
HABITAT: humid sites on the upper borders of the low zone, the laurel and pine forests. (400 to 1.800 m.)
COMMENTS: found only on the central and western islands.

Brachythecium rutabulum (Hedw.) B.S.G.

FAMILY: Hypnaceae
HABITAT: shaded sites of the laurel and fayal-brezal forests.
COMMENTS: present on the central and western islands.

LIVERWORTS

Lunularia cruciata (L.) Dum. ex Lindb

FAMILIA: Marchantiaceae
HABITAT: forms dense carpets on damp soil and rocks of the forests.
COMMENTS: present only on the central and western islands .

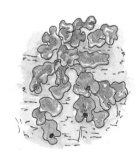

15

Marchantia polymorpha L.

FAMILY: Marchantiaceae
HABITAT: on the soil in very damp conditions; close to springs, water channels and damp rocks. Found mostly in the laurel forests between 300 and 1.400 m.
COMMENTS: central and western islands only.

Lophocolea cuspidata Limpr.

FAMILY: Jungermamniaceae
HABITAT: very damp areas of the Laurisilva.
COMMENTS: fairly rare.

Diplophyllum albicans (L.) Dum.

FAMILY: Jungermamniaceae
HABITAT: damp soil, rocks and trees in shaded areas of the laurel forest.
COMMENTS: found only on the western Canary Islands.

BUN BOLETE
Boletus edulis Bull.: Fr.

FAMILY: Boletaceae
HABITAT: humid woodlands, pine and chestnut forests.
COMMENTS: highly sought after for its culinary value.

Coltricia perennis (L.: Fr.) Murril

FAMILY: Hymenochaetaceae
HABITAT: appears after fire in the drier forests.
COMMENTS: inedible.

FIELD MUSHROOM
*Agaricus campestri*s L.: Fr.

FAMILY: Agaricaceae
HABITAT: in various habitats during the autumn and winter.
COMMENTS: one of the best species to eat.

JAPANESE UMBRELLA
Coprinus plicatilis (Curt.: Fr.) Fr.

FAMILY: Coprinaceae
HABITAT: found occasionally in the laurel and damp pine forests.
COMMENTS: soil dwelling species.

FLY AGARIC
Amanita muscaria (L.: Fr.) Quél.

FAMILY: Amanitaceae
HABITAT: pine and *Eucalyptus* forests and dry areas. Very rare.
COMMENTS: characteristic red cap signals the high toxicity of this species.

ST. GEORGE'S MUSHROOM
Tricholoma saponaceum (Fr.) Kumm.

FAMILY: Tricholomataceae
HABITAT: varied habitats, including pine and laurel forests. Appears in the autumn and winter.
COMMENTS: inedible.

WOODY BRACKET FUNGUS
Ganoderma applanatum (Pers.: Wallr.) Pat.

FAMILY: Ganodermataceae
HABITAT: tree trunks in the laurel forests, especially on old examples of Laurus azorica.
COMMENTS: relatively common.

CARPET FUNGUS
Thelephora terrestris Fr.

FAMILY: Thelephoraceae
HABITAT: fairly common in the forests.
COMMENTS: inedible with a foul stench.

ZONED BRACKET FUNGUS
Trametes versicolor (L.: Fr.) Pílat.

FAMILY: Polyphoraceae
HABITAT: common on tree trunks in the pine and laurel forests.
COMMENTS: inedible. Colour varies considerably.

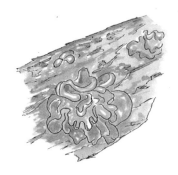

JELLY BRAIN FUNGUS
Tremella mesenterica Retz.

FAMILY: Tremellaceae
HABITAT: on dead wood in forests and *Eucalyptus* plantations.
COMMENTS: inedible.

CHANTERELLE
Cantharellus cibarius Fr.

FAMILY: Cantharellaceae
HABITAT: amongst the leaf litter of damp forests.
COMMENTS: appears after rain in the autumn.

EARTH STAR
Astraeus hygrometricus (Pers.) Morg.

FAMILY: Astraceae
HABITAT: amongst dry leaf litter of open forest and *Cistus* vegetation.
COMMENTS: rare.

FUNGI (CONT.)

Bovista plumbea   Pers.

FAMILY: Lycoperdaceae
HABITAT: in both wet and dry conditions from the coast to the pine forests.
COMMENTS: appears during the winter.

Lycoperdum perlatum   Pers.

FAMILY: Lycoperdaceae
HABITAT: typical of the forests.
COMMENTS: edible while small. Present in the winter.

LICHENS

Teloschistes flavicans   (Sw.) Norm.

FAMILY: Teloschistaceae
HABITAT: on trees in laurel and pine forests and olive groves.
COMMENTS: found on all the islands except Lanzarote.

Xanthoria parietina (L.) Beltr.

FAMILY: Teloschistaceae
HABITAT: on all types of substrate.
COMMENTS: cosmopolitan, found in all the temperate regions of the world.

Xanthoria resendei Poelt. & Tav

FAMILY: Teloschistaceae
HABITAT: in low arid areas.
COMMENTS: present on all the Canary Islands.

Squamarina crassa (Huds.) Poelt

FAMILY: Lecanoraceae
HABITAT: normally found growing on soil, but occasionally on rock.
COMMENTS: found on all the islands.

Lecanora sulphurella

FAMILY: Lecanoraceae
HABITAT: arid areas, on relatively recent lava.
COMMENTS: found on all the islands.

Ochrolechia parella (L.) Massal.

FAMILY: Lecanoraceae
HABITAT: on stones in the low and middle parts of the island.
COMMENTS: present on all the Canary Islands.

ORCHILLA
Roccella vicentina Vain.

FAMILY: Roccellaceae
HABITAT: tied to coastal environments, with certain halophile tendencies.
COMMENTS: used in the manufacture of dye. Known locally as "Orchilla".

LICHENS (CONT.)

Lethariella canariensis Moris

FAMILY: Usneaceae
HABITAT: high zones between 1.000 and 1.800 m., growing on trees and less frequently, rocks.
COMMENTS: an endemic of Macaronesia.

Stereocaulon vesuvianum Pers.

FAMILY: Stereocaulaceae
HABITAT: a pioneering species found on recent volcanic rock.
COMMENTS: present in both hemispheres, especially volcanic regions.

BLUE GREEN ALGAE

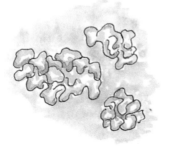

Calothrix crustacea (Thur). B. & F.

HABITAT: along the coast, within range of the sea spray.
COMMENTS: present on all the islands, and easiest to see during the summer

Caulerpa prolifera   (Fors.) Lamouroux

HABITAT: common on sandy substrates.
COMMENTS: present in inter-tidal pools with sandy deposits as well as on sandy bottoms.

Caulerpa racemosa   (Forssk.) J. Agardh.

HABITAT: rock pool walls and vertical rocks of the first few metres of the infralittoral.
COMMENTS: present on all the islands.

Chaetomorpha linum   O.F. Müller.

HABITAT: tangled around other seaweeds.
COMMENTS: found around all the islands.

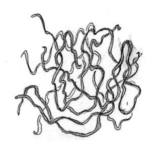

GREEN ALGAE (CHLOROPHYTA) (CONT.)

Cladophora prolifera   (Roth) Kütz

HABITAT: common, forming dark green masses on platforms and other poorly lit areas of the inter-tidal zone
COMMENTS: found around all the islands.

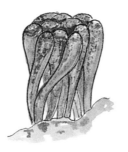

Dasycladus vermicularis   (Scop.) Krasser

HABITAT: common in ther inter-tidal zone.
COMMENTS: dark green and spongy. Often forming club-shaped colonies.

SEA MOSS
Bryopsis plumosa   (Huds.) C.A.Ag.

HABITAT: in pools of the inter-tidal zone.
COMMENTS: light green and feather-like.

Codium tomentosum   (Hunds.) Stackh.

HABITAT: on the bottom of pools in the lower inter-tidal zone.
COMMENTS: a dark green species.

GRASS KELP
Enteromorpha compressa   (L.) Grev.

HABITAT: pools of the inter-tidal zone.
COMMENTS: very common yet highly variable, a shiny green turning to white in the summer.

Enteromorpha intestinalis   (L.) Ness.

HABITAT: pools of the high inter-tidal zone.
COMMENTS: found around all the islands.

Caulerpa webbiana   Montagne

HABITAT: on rockpool platforms and vertical walls.
COMMENTS: a relatively common tropical species which forms bright, green lawns. Present around all the islands.

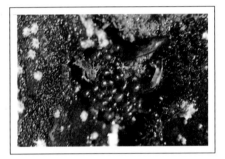

Valonia utricularis   (Roth) C. Agardh

HABITAT: common in the inter-tidal zones of all the islands.
COMMENTS: forms small bladders, in extensive dark green colonies .

Dasycladus vermicularis (Scopp.) Krasser

HABITAT: common in the intertidal zone of all the islands.
COMMENTS: dark green species, generally forming club-shaped colonies

Codium adhaerens (Cabrera) C. Agardh

HABITAT: rocks and walls of the lower inter-tidal zone and infralittoral. Common around all the islands in wave-swept, exposed areas.
COMMENTS: common in the inter-tidal zone, in pools and on rocks.

SEA LETTUCE
Ulva rigida C. Agardh.

HABITAT: common in the inter-tidal zone, on rocks and in pools.
COMMENTS: present around all the islands.

Enteromorpha ramulosa (Sm.) Hook

HABITAT: pools and rocks of the high inter-tidal zone, sometimes found growing on other algae.
COMMENTS: has a densely branched stem with multiple spine-like branches.

BROWN ALGAE (PHAEOPHYTA)

Colpomenia sinuosa   (Roth.) Derb. & Sol.

HABITAT: covers platforms of the inter-tidal and infralittoral zones.
COMMENTS: common around all the islands.

Scytosiphon lomentaria   (Clemente)

HABITAT: wave lashed areas of the inter-tidal zone.
COMMENTS: brown seaweed with tubular stems, narrowing at intervals.

FLAT WRACK
Dictyopteris membranaceae   (Stackhouse) Batters.

HABITAT: on the bottom of inter-tidal pools with low light intensity.
COMMENTS: brownish-yellow species, up to 15 cm. high.

Taonia atomaria   J.G. Agardh.

HABITAT: areas of low light intensity in the inter-tidal and infralittoral zones.
COMMENTS: brown stem with irregular branches. Reaches 30 cm.

Zonaria tournefortii (LAM.) Montagne.

HABITAT: inter-tidal zones of all the islands.
COMMENTS: a large species, reaching a length of 22 cm, with wide, brown, branches.

Cystoseira compressa   (Esper) G. & N.

HABITAT : common in the lower inter-tidal zone.
COMMENTS: polymorphic species up to 50 cm. long. Dimorphic, with short, wide rosettes during the winter and long erect stems in the summer.

Cystoseira humilis Kützing

HABITAT: typical of small rockpools in the intertidal zone.
COMMENTS: an Atlantic species which has a characteristic pyramidal form, present on all the islands.

Sargassum desfontainesii (Turner) C. Agardh.

HABITAT: common in the infra-littoral zone down to 18 m.
COMMENTS: large, greenish brown, Atlantic species, reaching lengths of 80 cm.

SARGASSO WEED
Sargassum vulgare S. Ag.

HABITAT: sometimes found in inter-tidal pools, but most common in the upper infra-littoral zone.
COMMENTS:branched, brown, poly-morphic species up to 90 cm. high, branched

BROWN SEAWEEDS (CONT.)

Hydroclathrus clathratus (Bory) M. Howe

HABITAT: intertidal zone and the upper part of the infralittoral, not common.
COMMENTS: brown and globular in form with round perforations, yellowish brown.

Halopteris scoparia (L.) Sauvag.

HABITAT: abundant both in the intertidal zone and below.
COMMENTS: characterised by its compact stems which form large dark brown masses up to 15 cm. high.

Dictyota dichotoma (Huds.) Lamour.

HABITAT: frequent in the upper infralittoral zone and in intertidal pools.
COMMENTS: stems brown. This is an iridescent species especially when in the juvenile stage.

Lobophora variegata   Lamour.

HABITAT: rock faces and holes in the infralittoral zone and at the edges of intertidal pools.
COMMENTS: a plant with a spreading, dark brown thallus.

PEACOCK'S TAIL
Padina pavonica   (L.) Lamour

HABITAT: abundant in the intertidal zone as well as in the upper part of the infralittoral in sheltered places   not affected by strong wave motion.
COMMENTS: a disc-shaped thallus which is whitish brown and calcareous.

Cystoseira abies-marina   (Turner) C. Ag.

HABITAT: very frequent in well lit areas at the upper limits of the tides.
COMMENTS: rough, almost spiny, yellowish stems which are often iridescent. It can grow to 80 cm. in length.

BROWN SEAWEEDS (CONT.)

Cystoseira compressa   (Esper) G. & N.

HABITAT: common in the lower reaches of the intertidal zone of all the islands.
COMMENTS: polymorphic species up to 50 cm. in height, not very branched, brown coloration.

RED SEAWEEDS (RHODOPHYTA)

Asparagopsis armata   Harv.

HABITAT: on the seabed and in pools in the intertidal zone especially in somewhat exposed conditions.
COMMENTS: present on the coasts of all the islands.

Griffithsia phyllamphora   J. Agardh

HABITAT: generally grows sheltered amongst other algae.
COMMENTS: a delicate, pinkish species which grows up to 4 cm. in height.

35

Spyridia filamentosa (Wulfen) Harvin Hook

HABITAT: frequent in intertidal pools in well illuminated places.
COMMENTS: the stem is pink to almost colourless, branched forming dense masses up to 15 cm. high.

Gelidium arbuscula Bory

HABITAT: usually found sheltering under other algae such as *Cystoseira abies-marina* on the north coasts of the islands.
COMMENTS: an Atlantic species from tropical and subtropical regions.

Gelidium latifolium (Greville) B. & T.

HABITAT: common in the intertidal zone
COMMENTS: an Atlantic species which is very frequent on the exposed coasts of the islands where it forms grass-like mats.

Pterocladia capillacea (Gmelin) B. & T.

HABITAT: in intertidal pools at the tidal limits and in the upper reaches of the infralittoral zone.
COMMENTS: very common in the Canary Islands.

Platoma cyclocolpa (Montagne) Shmitz

HABITAT: protected or sheltered areas of the intertidal zone and the upper infralittoral.
COMMENTS: has a gelatinous, flattened, pinkish red thallus with irregular branches and proliferations.

Plocamium cartilagineum (L.) Dixon

HABITAT: frequent on rocks and in crevices in the lower intertidal zone and the infralittoral.
COMMENTS: flat and gelatinous, up to 15 cm. in height.

Scinaia furcellata (Turn.) Bivona

HABITAT: frequent in sheltered localities.
COMMENTS: stem a deep wine-red, up to 15 cm. in height

Rhodymenia pseudopalmata (Lamouroux) Silva

HABITAT: in crevices and on shady rocks in the intertidal zone.
COMMENTS: the flat stem is small and pinkish in colour.

Laurencia obtusa (Hudson) Lamour.

HABITAT: frequent in pools on coastal platforms in the intertidal zone.
COMMENTS: the stem, which can reach 17 cm. long, is dark red or greenish, branched and pyramidal in form.

Asparagopsis taxiformis (Delile) Tr.

HABITAT: on the sheltered seabed and in pools in the lower intertidal zone.
COMMENTS: present on all the islands of the Canarian archipelago.

Corallina elongata   J. Ellis & Sol.

HABITAT: very common in the intertidal zone where it forms large mat-like populations.
COMMENTS: the articulated stem is deep pink and calcified, it is regularly pinnately branched.

Haliptilon virgata (Zanardin) G. & J.

HABITAT: frequent on the intertidal platforms and in the infralittoral zone, often on other seaweeds. Up to 5 cm. high.
COMMENTS: forms dense populations Present on all the islands and islets.

RED SEAWEEDS (CONT.)

Galaxaura lapidescens (Ellis & Sol.)Lamour

HABITAT: present in the intertidal zone.
COMMENTS: stem with filaments, branched habit reaching 9 cm. Present on all the islands.

FERNS AND ALLIES (PTERIDOPHYTA)

HORSETAIL
Equisetum ramosisimum   Desf.

FAMILY: Equisetaceae
HABITAT: common in humid localities, near streams and pools, water canals etc.
COMMENTS: closely related to the ferns.

GOLDEN RUSTY-BACK FERN
Ceterach aureum   (Cav.) Buch.

FAMILY: Aspleniaceae
HABITAT: a rather rare species wich occurs in the forest zones usually in crevices on rock faces.
COMMENTS: used in traditional medicine

ATLANTIC ISLANDS POLYPODY
Polypodium macaronesicum   Bobrov.

FAMILY: Polypodiaceae
HABITAT: common on rocks and walls
from the lower zone to the forests.
COMMENTS: frequent on the western
islands.

MAIDEN-HAIR FERN
Adiantum capillus-veneris   L.

FAMILY: Adiantaceae
HABITAT: frequent on humid rocks
and near springs in the forests and in
water canals and storage tanks in the
lower zone.
COMMENTS: cultivated as an ornamental fern.

KIDNEY FERN
Adiantum reniforme   L.

FAMILY: Adiantaceae
HABITAT: shady crevices and rock
faces in the lower and forest zones of the
western and central islands between
150 and 600 m.
COMMENTS: the leaf-shape is unmis-
takable.

FALSE BUCKLER FERN
Christella dentata   (Forssk.) Brownsey & Jermy

FAMILY: Thelipteridaceae
HABITAT: common in humid habitats, close to streams and pools in the forests or on the edges of water canals.
COMMENTS: usually a rather rare species.

RUSTY CLOAK FERN
Cheilanthes marantae   (L.) Domin.

FAMILY: Sinopteridaceae
HABITAT: present in the upper reaches of the lower zone and in forests.
COMMENTS: quite common, only on the western and central islands.

CHAIN FERN
Woodwardia radicans   (L.) J. E. Sm.

FAMILY: Blechnaceae
HABITAT: cliffs, walls and slopes in the wettest areas of the laurel forest.
COMMENTS: sometimes found grown as an ornamental on the islands and in European glasshouses.

CUPRESSACEAE

CANARY JUNIPER
Juniperus canariensis Guyot

SIZE: small tree up to 8 m.
DESCRIPTION: triangular, scale-like lea-
ves, dark red globular cones.
HABITAT: forms "sabinares" in the north
between 300-700m.
COMMENTS: Abundant and typical of the
Gomera landscape.
CONSERVATION STATUS: LR

SALICACEAE

CANARY WILLOW
Salix canariensis Chr. Sm.

SIZE: Shrub/tree up to 10 m.
DESCRIPTION: alternate lanceolate lea-
ves, flowers in catkins up to 6cm long.
HABITAT: stream- sides, especially in the
beds of ravines.
COMMENTS: Bark, leaves and flowers
used in local medicine.
CONSERVATION STATUS: LR

MYRICACEAE

WAX MYRTLE
Myrica faya Aiton

SIZE: shrub/tree up to 10 m.
DESCRIPTION: oblanceolate leaves with
revolute borders, reddish to black, fleshy
fruits.
HABITAT: Common in humid forests associated with brezo (*Erica arborea*) and in the
laurisilvia, between 500 and 1.500m..
COMMENTS: fruits formed part of the
ancient Guanche inhabitant's diet, the
wood was used for charcoal.
CONSERVATION STATUS: LR

URTICACEAE

CANARY ISLANDS NETTLE
Urtica morifolia Poir.

SIZE: up to 1 m.
DESCRIPTION: heart-shaped, opposite leaves with stinging hairs. Inflorescences axilliary.
HABITAT: Forests between 500-1.400 m. Laurisilvia. Colonizer of disturbed areas.
COMMENTS: Despite its severe sting, used medicinally against tuberculosis and as a hair tonic.
CONSERVATION STATUS: LR

TREE PELLITORY
Gesnouinia arborea (L.) Gaudich

SIZE: Shrub/small tree up to 3 m.
DESCRIPTION: Large prominently veined leaves. Pinkish, paniculate inflorescences, small star shaped flowers.
HABITAT: laurel forests between 600-1.200 m.
COMMENTS: Common at Los Chorros de Epina.
CONSERVATION STATUS: LR

POLYGONACEAE

CANARY SORREL
Rumex lunaria L.

SIZE: shrub up to 2 m.
DESCRIPTION: glaucous, oval leaves, truncated at the base. Paniculate, reddish inflorescences.
HABITAT: low areas, forests, roadsides, etc. Very common.
COMMENTS: Used locally as a decongestant and anti-inflammatory.
CONSERVATION STATUS: LR

CARYOPHYLLACEAE

GOMERAN CAMPION
Silene bourgaei Webb ex Christ

SIZE: up to 60 cm.
DESCRIPTION: small plant with lanceolate leaves and white flowers.
HABITAT:North coast cliffs up to 500 m. Agulo and Hermigua.
COMMENTS: endemic, exclusive to the island.
CONSERVATION STATUS: LR

SUCCULENT ALL-SEED
Polycarpaea carnosa Chr. Sm.

SIZE: Stems to 40 cm.
DESCRIPTION: rupicolous hanging plant, rounded fleshy leaves. Inflorescences terminal.
HABITAT: northeast region, Barranco de La Villa, La Vieja. 50-500 m.
COMMENTS: leaves used in the islands as a diuretic.
CONSERVATION STATUS: LR

COMMON ALLSEED
Polycarpaea teneriffae Lam.

SIZE: up to 30 cm.
DESCRIPTION: creeping with variable, spathulate leaves. Large ,very branched inflorescences .
HABITAT: low areas and forests, especially alongside paths. Between 5-1000 m.
COMMENTS: Common over most of the island.
CONSERVATION STATUS: LR

CARYOPHYLLACEAE (cont.)

GOMERAN ALL-SEED
Dicheranthus plocamoides   Webb

SIZE: dwarf shrub up to 30 cm.
DESCRIPTION: linear succulent lea-
ves, erect   stems, terminal inflores-
cences.
HABITAT: North coast from San
Sebastian to Valle Gran Rey, up to 400
m. Common in Vallehermoso.
COMMENTS: a good rockery plant.
CONSERVATION STATUS: LR

RANUNCULACEAE

ATLANTIC ISLANDS BUTTERCUP
Ranunculus cortusifolius   Willd.

SIZE: up to 60 cm.
DESCRIPTION: herbaceous. Large
orbiculate or heart shaped, rough lea-
ves, Bright, yellow 5-petalled flowers.
HABITAT: forests of the centre. El
Cedro, Agando, Epina to Arure.
COMMENTS: used   medicinally
against haemorrhoids, as a painkiller
CONSERVATION STATUS: LR

LAURACEAE

CANARY LAURELor BAY
Laurus azorica   (Seub.) Franco

SIZE: tree between 15-20 m.
DESCRIPTION: aromatic, glandular
leaves, cream flowers. Produces oval,
black berries with a single seed.
HABITAT: humid forests between 500-
1.500 m. El Cedro, etc.
COMMENTS: the most abundant tree
in the forests.
CONSERVATION STATUS: LR

LAURACEAE (cont.)

MADEIRA LAUREL, GREENHEART
Ocotea foetens   (Aiton) Benth.

SIZE: tree to 30 m.
DESCRIPTION: leaves widely lance-
olate or oval with two glands at the
base. Fruits similar to acorns.
HABITAT: in humid forests. El Cedro,
Arure, Agando and Vallehermoso.
COMMENTS: strong smelling wood
with a texture similar to ebony.
CONSERVATION STATUS: LR

CANARY ISLANDS EBONY
Persea indica   (L.) Spreng.

SIZE: tree up to 20 m.
DESCRIPTION: pale green, lanceolate
leaves without glands. Elliptical fruits 2
cm. long, ripening to blue-black.
HABITAT: humid forests. El Cedro,
Arure, Agando and Vallehermoso.
COMMENTS: possibly the most
attractive tree in the forests.
CONSERVATION STATUS: LR

CANARY MAHOGANY
Apollonias barbujana (Cav.) Bornm.

SIZE: Tree to 25 m.
DESCRIPTION: dark green, shiny, lan-
ceolate to oval leaves without glands.
HABITAT: humid forests, Laurisilvia.
COMMENTS: wood once used locally
to make very good quality furniture.
CONSERVATION STATUS: LR

LAURACEAE *(cont.)*

BLACK MAHOGANY
Apollonias ceballosi   Svent.

SIZE: Tree up to 25 m.
DESCRIPTION: shiny,dark green, oval and glandless leaves, hermaphrodite flowers and oval berries.
HABITAT: humid forests. Riscos de Epina. 600-1.000 m.
COMMENTS: endemic exclusive to La Gomera.
CONSERVATION STATUS: VU

CRUCIFERAE

GOMERAN SEA-KALE
Crambe gomerae   Webb ex Christ

SIZE: Shrub up to 1 m.
DESCRIPTION: rough lanceolate or oval, petiolate leaves.
HABITAT: Eastern region from the Barranco de La Villa to Tagamiche and Roque Agando.
COMMENTS: endemic exclusive to La Gomera
CONSERVATION STATUS: LR

GOMERA SHRUBBY STOCK
Parolinia schizogynoides   Svent.

SIZE: dwarf shrub up to 80 cm.
DESCRIPTION: linear leaves.
Inflorescences of up to 20 flowers.
HABITAT: Southeastern region, Valle de Argaga. 200-350 m.
COMMENTS: the genus *Parolinia* is endemic to the Canaries, with most of the 7 species on Gran Canaria.
CONSERVATION STATUS: EN

CRUCIFERAE *(cont.)*

WALL FLOWER
Erysimum bicolor (Hornem.) DC.

SIZE: up to 50 cm.
DESCRIPTION: linear to lanceolate leaves. Lax inflorescences.
HABITAT: low areas and forests up to 1.000 m.
COMMENTS: ornamental value. Cultivated as a garden plant.
CONSERVATION STATUS: LR

ROSACEAE

RED SHRUBBY BURNET
Marcetella moquiniana (Webb & Berth.)

SIZE: shrub up to 3 m.
DESCRIPTION: upper stems glandular with red hairs. Leaves in terminal rosettes.
HABITAT: between 300-600 m.
COMMENTS: very rare in La Gomera.
CONSERVATION STATUS: VU

RHAMNACEAE

CANARY ISLANDS BUCKTHORN
Rhamnus glandulosa Aiton

SIZE: tree to 10 m.
DESCRIPTION: oval leaves with small but prominent round glands at the vein joints. Globular red-black fruit.
HABITAT: El Cedro, Chorros de Epina to Arure. Common.
COMMENTS: ornamental potential.
CONSERVATION STATUS: LR

CRASSULACEAE

VALLEHERMOSO HOUSELEEK
Aeonium castello-paivae Bolle

SIZE: up to 25 cm.
DESCRIPTION: cream-white flowers and glaucous leaves.
HABITAT: low areas on rock slopes.
COMMENTS: endemic, exclusive to the island.
CONSERVATION STATUS: LR

RED HOUSELEEK
Aeonium decorum Webb ex Bolle

SIZE: up to 20 cm.
DESCRIPTION: small, much branched, spreading shrub with glabrous reddish leaves.
HABITAT: between 100-500 m. Barranco de la VilLa, Barranco de La Laja, Valle Gran Rey, etc.
COMMENTS: exclusive to La Gomera
CONSERVATION STATUS: LR

GOMERA HOUSELEEK
Aeonium gomerense Praeger

SIZE: shrub up to 1 m.
DESCRIPTION: very succulent, glabrous leaves in rosettes up to 20 cm. in diameter with red tinged edges. Flowers white.
HABITAT: Barranco de la Villa between San Sebastian and Hermigua. On steep rocky slopes. 600-1.000 m.
COMMENTS: exclusive to La Gomera.
CONSERVATION STATUS: EN

CRASSULACEAE (cont.)

RED-LINED HOUSELEEK
Aeonium rubrolineatum Svent.

SIZE: to 50 cm.
DESCRIPTION: succulent with pastel-pink flowers in summer.
HABITAT: between 600- 1.200 m.
COMMENTS: exclusive to La Gomera.
CONSERVATION STATUS: VU

STICKY HOUSELEEK
Aeonium viscatum Webb ex Bolle

SIZE: shrub up to 40 cm.
DESCRIPTION: glabrous, sticky, succulent leaves. Yellow flowers.
HABITAT:Northeastern region from the coast to 500 m. San Sebastian, La Laja, Agulo, Roque Cano and Puerto de Vallehermoso.
COMMENTS: endemic to La Gomera.
CONSERVATION STATUS: LR

SESSILE HOUSELEEK
Aeonium subplanum Praeger

SIZE: up to 20 cm.
DESCRIPTION: flattened rosettes of layered, broad tipped spathulate leaves.
HABITAT: between 200-1.100 m. North of the island, from San Sebastian to Valle Gran Rey.
COMMENTS: exclusive to the island.
CONSERVATION STATUS: LR

CRASSULACEAE (cont.)

SAUNDER'S HOUSELEEK
Aeonium saundersii   Bolle

SIZE: shrublet to 20 cm.
DESCRIPTION: suborbiculate leaves, densely pubescent on both sides.
HABITAT: dry cliffs near La Laja. New populations recently discovered in the south and west
COMMENTS: exclusive to La Gomera
CONSERVATION STATUS: VU

STONECROP HOUSELEEK
Monanthes laxiflora   (D.C.) Bolle

SIZE: only 10 cm.
DESCRIPTION: hanging or creeping plant, opposite leaves silver-grey, sometimes dark green. Flowers yellow to pink.
HABITAT: low areas, forests to 1.200 m.
COMMENTS: Canarian endemic, found on all the islands.
CONSERVATION STATUS: LR

MINIATURE HOUSELEEK
Monanthes amydros   Svent.

SIZE: tiny, 2 cm.
DESCRIPTION: cushion-like rosettes. Leaves up to 6 mm. rosettes to 1.5 cm.
HABITAT: North side, Barranco de La Villa, Majona, Agulo, Vallehermoso, Epina, etc. 20-180 m.
COMMENTS: exclusive to La Gomera.
CONSERVATION STATUS: LR

ANNUAL HOUSELEEK
Aichryson laxum (Haw.) Bramwell

SIZE: up to 35 cm.
DESCRIPTION: slightly downy, erect annual or biannual. Somewhat fleshy, very hairy leaves arranged in sub-rosettes. Flowers yellow.
HABITAT: forests and other shaded areas between 200 and 400 m.
COMMENTS: Canarian endemic, absent only from Lanzarote and Fuerteventura.
CONSERVATION STATUS: LR

GOLDEN HOUSELEEK
Greenovia diplocycla Webb ex Bolle

SIZE: up to 20 cm.
DESCRIPTION: forms unbranched rosettes. Leaf borders slightly ciliated.
HABITAT: low zone and forest cliffs between 50 and 1.200 m.
COMMENTS: endemic, on the western islands
CONSERVATION STATUS: LR

GOLDEN HOUSELEEK
Greenovia aurea (Ch. Sm.) W. & B.

SIZE: up to 15 cm.
DESCRIPTION: in dense rosettes of blue-green leaves. Short stemmed. Flowers have 30 to 35 petals.
HABITAT: cliffs, walls and dry slopes at all altitudes. Rare on La Gomera.
COMMENTS: useful garden plant on rockeries and stone walls.
CONSERVATION STATUS: LR

BIRD'SFOOT TREFOIL
Lotus emeroides   R.P. Murray

SIZE: up to 15 cm.
DESCRIPTION: perennial with trifoliate leaves. Yellow flowers in groups of 3 to 5, petals sometimes tipped with purple.
HABITAT: slopes and cliffs up to 500 m. Locally abundant.
COMMENTS: exclusive to La Gomera.
CONSERVATION STATUS: LR

GOMERA BROOM
Teline gomerae (Gibbs & Dingwall) Kunk.

SIZE: up to 2 m.
DESCRIPTION: shrub, leaves trifoliate, each leaflet oblong to lanceolate. Dense inflorescences of up to 60 yellow flowers.
HABITAT: in the transition between the low and brezal/sabinal zone. 400 to 600 m.
COMMENTS: uncommon species with ornamental and possible forage value.
CONSERVATION STATUS: VU

LA PALMA BROOM
Teline stenopetala Webb & Berth.

SIZE: grows to 6 m.
DESCRIPTION: petiolate leaves with elliptical or lanceolate leaflets.
HABITAT: laurisilva forest and fayal-brezal borders, between 400 and 600 m.
COMMENTS: of medicinal and forage value. Canarian endemic.
CONSERVATION STATUS: LR

LEGUMINOSAE *(cont.)*

STICKY BROOM
Adenocarpus foliolosus (Ait.) DC.

SIZE: up to 3 m.
DESCRIPTION: erect, luxuriant shrub with bunches of terminal, yellow flowers. Glandular seed pods.
HABITAT: borders of pine and laurel forests up to 1.600 m.
COMMENTS: Canarian endemic, on all islands but Lanzarote and Fuerteventura.
CONSERVATION STATUS: LR

WHITE BROOM
Spartocytisus filipes Webb & Berth.

SIZE: up to 2 m.
DESCRIPTION: small, slender stemmed shrub with trifoliate leaves. Flowers white, pod black and hairy.
HABITAT: shaded sites in the low zone and paths of the Laurisilva. 500-800 m.
COMMENTS: species and genus endemic to the western islands. Yields very hard wood. Flowers attract bees.
CONSERVATION STATUS: LR

TAGASASTE
Chamaecytisus proliferus (L.) Link

SIZE: reaches 4 m.
DESCRIPTION: shrub or small tree,, very variable in size, leaf colour and hairiness. White flowers in fascicles. Pod black.
HABITAT: in forest areas, especially the borders of the Laurisilva.
COMMENTS: often cultivated and used as forage.
CONSERVATION STATUS: LR

GERANIACEAE

CANARY ISLANDS CRANESBILL
Geranium canariense Reut.

SIZE: reaches 50 cm.
DESCRIPTION: herbaceous, occasionally with a woody base. Leaves deeply lobed, arranged in a large rosette. Pink flowers 2-3 cm. in diameter.
HABITAT: common and typical of laurel and Fayal/Brezal forests between 500 and 1.000 m.
COMMENTS: grown as an ornamental.
CONSERVATION STATUS: LR

EUPHORBIACEAE

BERTHELOT'S SPURGE
Euphorbia berthelotii Bolle

SIZE: up to 2 m.
DESCRIPTION: shrub with succulent reddish stems, glaucous leaves and yellow-green inflorescences.
HABITAT: locally frequent in the low zone of the Southeast, where it forms extensive "tabaibales".
COMMENTS: endemic to La Gomera. Produces poisonous latex.
CONSERVATION STATUS: LR

BRAVO'S SPURGE
Euphorbia bravoana Svent.

SIZE: up to 2 m.
DESCRIPTION: shrub. Leaves glaucous, reddish surrounding the inflorescence. Flowers in purplish umbels.
HABITAT: Confined to a few barrancos of the Northeast, between Agulo and San Sebastian.
COMMENTS: a rare island endemic, named after the local professor and conservationist, Dr. Ventura Bravo.
CONSERVATION STATUS: VU

EUPHORBIACEAE *(cont.)*

LEAFLESS SPURGE
Euphorbia aphylla Brouss. ex Willd.

SIZE: up to 35 cm.
DESCRIPTION: small, compact, leafless shrub, with slender, succulent stems and small, insignificant flowers.
HABITAT: halophile species of the rocky coast and slopes facing the sea. 0 to 50 m.
COMMENTS: Canarian endemic, typical of the north coasts with *Aeonium viscatum.*
CONSERVATION STATUS: LR

SWEET SPURGE
Euphorbia balsamifera Ait.

SIZE: reaches 2.5 m.
DESCRIPTION: grey stemmed shrub, short, glaucous, green leaves, flowers solitary, capsules brown.
HABITAT: common on the coast, especially near the sea and on dry slopes, where if forms extensive "tabaibales".
COMMENTS: found from North Africa to Yemen. Its latex is not poisonous.
CONSERVATION STATUS: LR

GOMERA SPURGE
Euphorbia lambii Svent.

SIZE: up to 2 m.
DESCRIPTION: glaucous or green leaved shrub, with large yellow inflorescences and light brown capsules.
HABITAT: on slopes bordering the Laurisilva and fayal/brezal between 600 and 800 m.
COMMENTS: one of the islands rarest endemics, unknown until 1960.
CONSERVATION STATUS: CR

MALVACEAE

TREE MALLOW
Lavatera acerifolia   Cav.

SIZE: grows to 2.5 m.
DESCRIPTION: shrub with palmate leaves. Flowers similar to those of *Hibiscus*, in small, terminal or auxilliary groups. Petals mauve, with darker bases.
HABITAT: cliffs and paths of the low zone, 250 to 500 m.
COMMENTS: of ornamental value.
CONSERVATION STATUS: LR

GUTTIFERAE

LARGE-LEAVED ST. JOHN'S WORT
Hypericum grandifolium   Choisy

SIZE: up to 1 m.
DESCRIPTION: shrub with large oval leaves; flowers yellow, up to 4.5 cm. with multiple stamens
HABITAT: in forests, path sides of the laurisilvia, etc. 400-1.500 m. Very common.
COMMENTS: A good garden plant.
CONSERVATION STATUS: LR

CANARY ST. JOHN'S WORT
Hypericum canariense   L.

SIZE: up to 2.5 m.
DESCRIPTION: tall shrub with variable leaves, 2 to 7 cm. long. Yellow flowers in terminal panicles, up to 2 cm. across.
HABITAT: forest zones, especially the fayal-brezal. Occasionally in sabinares, and on slopes in the low zone. 150 to 800 m.
COMMENTS: used medicinally and recommended as a garden plant.
CONSERVATION STATUS: LR

VIOLACEAE

MADEIRA VIOLET
Viola maderensis Lowe

SIZE: up to 10 cm.
DESCRIPTION: herbaceous, heart - shaped leaves and intense, violet flowers with paler spur.
HABITAT: in shaded areas of the laurel forests, with ferns and other deep shade plants.
COMMENTS: endemic to the Canaries and Madeira. Cultivated for its ornamental value.
CONSERVATION STATUS: LR

CISTACEAE

WHITE GUM
Cistus monspeliensis L.

SIZE: reaches 1.5 m.
DESCRIPTION: linear, sticky leaves with revolute borders and short lived white flowers.
HABITAT: very common in forest zones, colonizing cleared areas and the lower forest, borders , sabinares.
COMMENTS: widely distributed around the Mediterranean. Common on La Gomera.
CONSERVATION STATUS: LR

CANARY ISLANDS GUM
Cistus symphytifolius Lam.

SIZE: up to 1.5 m.
DESCRIPTION: variable shrub, with lanceolate or oval wrinkled and hairy leaves. Large flowers with 5 pink petals.
HABITAT: in the forests of the centre, between 800 and 1.200 m.
COMMENTS: Canarian endemic.
CONSERVATION STATUS:LR

TAMARICACEAE

TAMARISK
Tamarix canariensis Willd.

SIZE: up to 6 m.
DESCRIPTION: shrub to small tree with small, alternate, scale-like leaves. Pink flowers in spikes between 60 and 120 mm.
HABITAT: coastal zones and barrancos, forming small thickets and copses. 0 to 400 m.
COMMENTS: wood highly valued for carpentry.
CONSERVATION STATUS: LR

ARALIACEAE

CANARY ISLANDS IVY
Hedera canariensis Willd.

SIZE: UP to 6 m.
DESCRIPTION: woody creeper with large, simple or three lobed leaves, flowers in umbels, fruit round and black.
HABITAT: in rupicolous communities and on the ground or on dead trunks in the laurisilva.
COMMENTS: often grown to cover walls and pergolas.
CONSERVATION STATUS: VU

UMBELLIFERAE

HARE'S EAR
Bupleurum salicifolium   Soland.

SIZE: reaches 1.5 m.
DESCRIPTION: woody shrub with sharp, linear, lanceolate leaves, veins more or less parallel. Small, yellow flowers in umbels.
HABITAT: rupicolous plant, in crevices and ledges on the cliffs of the lower and forested zones. 100 to 1.000 m.
COMMENTS: on La Gomera the leaves are wider and the plant more robust than on the other islands.
CONSERVATION STATUS: LR

UMBELLIFERAE *(cont.)*

CANARY SAMPHIRE
Astydamia latifolia (L. Fil.) O. Kuntze

SIZE: up to 50 cm.
DESCRIPTION: perennial with thick, succulent, pinnate leaves, drying up in the summer. Yellow flowers in compound umbels. The fruit have a cork-like texture.
HABITAT: halophile, common on coastal cliffs.
COMMENTS: Canaries and Moroccan coast only.
CONSERVATION STATUS: LR

GOMERAN BURNET SAXIFRAGE
Pimpinella junoniae Ceb. & Ort.

SIZE: reaches 75 cm.
DESCRIPTION: woody based perennial, bipinnate leaves. Flowers in umbels of 7 to 10 rays.
HABITAT: cliffs of the high part of the dry zone and the lower forest boundaries. 600 to 1.200 m.
COMMENTS: plant with ornamental potential.
CONSERVATION STATUS: LR

MYRSINACEAE

CANARY ISLANDS ARDISIA
Heberdenia bahamensis (Gaertn.) Sprague

SIZE: grows up to 10 m.
DESCRIPTION: tree with oval, leathery leaves and strong smelling white flowers. Globular, red to black fruit.
HABITAT: in the Laurisilva, especially forest borders and cliffs. 500 to 1.000 m.
COMMENTS: exclusive to The Canaries and Madeira.
CONSERVATION STATUS: VU

ERICACEAE

RED TREE HEATH
Erica scoparia ssp. *platycodon* Webb & Berth.

SIZE: 3 m. or more.
DESCRIPTION: shrub with slightly revolute leaves. Pink to red flowers in terminal clusters.
HABITAT: humid areas of the Laurisilva and fayal-brezal, locally frequent in some areas.
COMMENTS: replaces the brezo in the most humid areas of the island (Chorros de Epina, Arure, etc.).
CONSERVATION STATUS: LR

TREE HEATH
Erica arborea L.

SIZE: reaches 15 m.
DESCRIPTION: shrub or small tree. Leaves 5 mm long, revolute. Large, dense inflorescences of white flowers.
HABITAT: forms forests with the wax-myrtle, very common in the humid, cloud zones.
COMMENTS: African and Mediterranean basin species, colonizing cleared forest areas.
CONSERVATION STATUS: LR

CANARY STRAWBERRY TREE
Arbutus canariensis Veil.

SIZE: up to 15 m.
DESCRIPTION: tree with red-brown bark, leaves with indented borders, fruits globular, orange. The flowers have pinkish-white, bell shaped corollas
HABITAT: edges and clearings of the Laurisilva.
COMMENTS: an ornamental tree, the fruit is rich in vitamin C.
CONSERVATION STATUS: VU

PLUMBAGINACEAE

GOMERA SEA-LAVENDER
Limonium redivivum (Svent.) Kunk. & Sund.

SIZE: up to 80 cm.
DESCRIPTION: rosetted plant with a woody base. Entire or slightly lobed, oval leaves. Inflorescences on winged stalks. Calyx blue.
HABITAT: steep cliffs of the west of the island, 600-1.000 m.
COMMENTS: very rare, of ornamental value
CONSERVATION STATUS: CR

TREE SEA-LAVENDER
Limonium dendroides Svent.

SIZE: from 1 to 3 m.
DESCRIPTION: shrub with large, green, lanceolate leaves. Pinkish flowers on wingless stalks.
HABITAT: on inaccessible cliffs in the Barrancos of Argaga and el Cabrito. Sporadic on the cliffs of the south. 50 to 500 m.
COMMENTS: among the rarest plants in the world, in extreme danger of extinction.
CONSERVATION STATUS: CR

CABBAGE-LEAVED SEA LAVENDER
Limonium brassicifolium (Webb & Berth.) O. Kuntze

SIZE: up to 80 cm.
DESCRIPTION: rosetted. Sinuous-lobulate leaves with large terminal lobule. Calyx pale mauve.
HABITAT: Northern cliffs between Agulo and Vallehermoso.
COMMENTS: Highly ornamental. A garden plant in Gran Canaria and Tenerife.
CONSERVATION STATUS: EN

OLEACEAE

WILD OLIVE
Olea europaea ssp. *cerasiformis* (W.& B.) Sund.

SIZE: up to 7 m.
DESCRIPTION: shrub or small tree, leaves narrowly lanceolate, with white undersides. White flowers and fruit that blacken on ripening.
HABITAT: the lower zone and sabinales, forming thickets at some sites. 50 to 700 m.
COMMENTS: popular medicinal plant, wood used for walking sticks.
CONSERVATION STATUS: LR

SOUTHERN OLIVE or PALO BLANCO
Picconia excelsa (Aiton) DC.

SIZE: up to 10 m.
DESCRIPTION: tree, whitish bark, opposite, oval leaves, white flowers, olive-like, black fruit.
HABITAT: laurisilva and sabinares, up to 1.000 m.
COMMENTS: wood appreciated for carpentry. Endemic to Madeira and the Canaries.
CONSERVATION STATUS: VU

CANARY JASMINE
Jasminum odoratissimum L.

SIZE: 1 to 4 m.
DESCRIPTION: shrub with pinnate, glossy leaves, yellow flowers and black berries.
HABITAT: generally found in the rocky areas of the thermophile forest and sabinares. 400 to 800 m.
COMMENTS: endemic to Madeira and the Canaries. Potential garden plant.
CONSERVATION STATUS: LR

ASCLEPIADACEAE

KRAINZ'S WAX PLANT
Ceropegia krainzii Svent.

SIZE: to 70 cm.
DESCRIPTION: cylindrical, olive-grey, succulent stems. Large groups of lemon yellow flowers.
HABITAT: on lower zone barranco cliffs between San Sebastian and Agulo, up to 600 m.
COMMENTS: endemic to La Gomera, rare and endangered by collectors
CONSERVATION STATUS: EN

GOMERA WAX PLANT
Ceropegia ceratophora Svent.

SIZE: up to 150 cm.
DESCRIPTION: olive-brown stems, pale green-lemon flowers in groups of 10 to 20. Flower lobules joined at the tip.
HABITAT: cliffs and slopes of the xerophytic southeast, between 600 and 1.000 m.
COMMENTS: very rare; endemic to La Gomera.
CONSERVATION STATUS: EN

CANARY SILK VINE
Periploca laevigata   Aiton

SIZE: creeper, stems up to 4 or 5 m.
DESCRIPTION: opposite leaves, flowers one cm. in diameter. Fruit horn-shaped.
HABITAT: commom in the tabaibales and cardonales(spurge shrubland) of the lower zone up to 600 m.
COMMENTS: common on all the islands and Morocco.
CONSERVATION STATUS: LR

RUBIACEAE

CANARY MADDER
Rubia fruticosa Aiton

SIZE: stems up to 4 m. long.
DESCRIPTION: polymorphic climbing shrub. Glossy leaves in groups of 4 with spiny edges. Black fruits.
HABITAT: lower zone in the spurge shrubland. Very common between 50 and 500 m.
COMMENTS: endemic, present on all the islands, has medicinal value.
CONSERVATION STATUS: LR

CAPITANA
Phyllis nobla L.

SIZE: up to 50 cm.
DESCRIPTION: small bush with entire, lanceolate or oval leaves. Small whitish flowers.
HABITAT: slopes and cliffs of the humid forest zones, between 600 and 1.200 m.
COMMENTS: endemic to Madeira and the Canaries.
CONSERVATION STATUS: LR

BALO
Plocama pendula Aiton

SIZE: reaches 2.5 m.
DESCRIPTION: shrub with pendulous stems, and filiform leaves. Globular, black fruit.
HABITAT: the driest barranco beds of the lower zone, to 500 m.
COMMENTS: foul smelling, endemic, found on all the islands.
CONSERVATION STATUS: LR

CONVOLVULACEAE

CANARY TREE BINDWEED
Convolvulus floridus L. fil.

SIZE: up to 3 m.
DESCRIPTION: shrub with linear-oblong leaves, 2 to 14 cm. long. White flowers in large panicles, up to 1 cm. wide.
HABITAT: slopes and ledges of the lower zone and the sabinares, up to 600 m.
COMMENTS: highly ornamental Canary endemic.
CONSERVATION STATUS: LR

GOMERA BINDWEED
Convolvulus subauriculatus (Burchd.) Lindinger

SIZE: creeper with stems to 2 m.
DESCRIPTION: elliptical leaves, subauriculate at the base.
HABITAT: cliffs of the lower zone, between 300 and 400 m.
COMMENTS: rare and endemic to La Gomera.
CONSERVATION STATUS: CR

FOREST BINDWEED
Convolvulus canariensis L.

SIZE: 6 m. or more.
DESCRIPTION: woody creeper with hairy, heart-shaped or oval leaves. Violet-blue flowers.
HABITAT: laurel forests between 500 and 1.000 m.
COMMENTS: Canary endemic typical of the most humid forests.
CONSERVATION STATUS: VU

BORAGINACEAE

ROUGH-LEAVED BUGLOSS
Echium strictum   L. fil.

SIZE: to 1 m.
DESCRIPTION: shrub with hispid, lanceolate leaves. Flowers reddish to intense blue in lax inflorescences.
HABITAT: Shaded sites in the lower zone and laurel forests, especially in clearings. 500 to 1.000 m.
COMMENTS: ssp. *gomerae* endemic to the island.
CONSERVATION STATUS: VU

WHITE BUGLOSS
Echium aculeatum   Poiret

SIZE: up to 150 cm.
DESCRIPTION: shrub with very spiny, linear leaves and dense inflorescences of white flowers.
HABITAT: common in lowland dry zones and tabaibales. 500 to 1.000 m.
COMMENTS: common and variable, endemic to the western islands.
CONSERVATION STATUS: LR

GOMERA BUGLOSS
Echium acanthocarpum   Svent.

SIZE: up to 150 cm.
DESCRIPTION:Shrub with brown bark and oval to lanceolate, hispid leaves. Large, dense, blue inflorescences.
HABITAT: laurel forest cliffs, 800 to 1.000 m.
COMMENTS: very rare, limited to La Gomera.
CONSERVATION STATUS: CR

LABIATAE

COMMON CANARY SAVORY
Micromeria varia   Benth.

SIZE: to 35 cm.
DESCRIPTION: pubescent shrub, opposite, fasciculate leaves. Purple or white flowers in lax inflorescences.
HABITAT: locally common in all zones from the coast to the mountains. Common in the Laurisilva and on pathways, 20 to 1.500 m.
COMMENTS: medicinal plant endemic to Madeira and the Canaries.
CONSERVATION STATUS: LR

GOMERA SAVORY
Micromeria lepida   Webb & Berth.

SIZE: up to 30 cm.
DESCRIPTION: dense shrublet with opposite, almost glabrous leaves. Pinkish corolla and long calyx (6 mm.)
HABITAT: generally in the forest zones with the variety *argagae* in the eastern dry zone, 400 to 1.200 m.
COMMENTS: endemic to La Gomera with a similar species (hairier with a pale corolla) in the lower zone.
CONSERVATION STATUS: LR

GOMERA FALSE SAGE
Sideritis gomeraea   De Noe ex Bolle

SIZE: up to 40 cm.
DESCRIPTION: rupicolous, hanging plant with white, woolly leaves. Long spikes of white flowers with brown lips.
HABITAT: cliffs of the lower zone and the lower limits of the forests. 250 to 900 m.
COMMENTS: endemic to La Gomera, has medicinal properties.
CONSERVATION STATUS: VU

LABIATAE (cont.)

VALLE GRAN REY FALSE SAGE
Sideritis nutans Svent.

SIZE: up to 30 cm.
DESCRIPTION: rupicolous, with short stems and green, glandular leaves; erect, drooping inflorescences and cream flowers with brown lips.
HABITAT: hills and cliffs of the lower zone, especially in the East. 200 to 700 m.
COMMENTS: endemic to La Gomera.
CONSERVATION STATUS: VU

SPIKED FALSE SAGE
Sideritis spicata (Pit.) Marrero

SIZE: up to 40 cm.
DESCRIPTION: small shrub, crenulate leaves with white, woolly undersides. Flowers in erect spikes, corolla with dark brown lips.
HABITAT: common on cliffs of the thermophile forests and tabaibales. 100 to 1.100 m.
COMMENTS: exclusive to La Gomera.
CONSERVATION STATUS: LR

ROQUE CAMPANA FALSE SAGE
Sideritis marmorea Bolle

SIZE: reaches 40 cm.
DESCRIPTION: small, woody plant with short stems, rounded, yellow-green, hairy leaves and erect spikes of white flowers with brown lips.
HABITAT: humid rocks and shaded areas of the Northeast. 300 to 500 m.
COMMENTS: very rare, endemic to La Gomera.
CONSERVATION STATUS: CR

LABIATAE (cont.)

ORIGANUM-LEAVED MINT
Bystropogon origanifolius L'Hér.

SIZE: up to 150 cm.
DESCRIPTION: variable bush, crenulate, lanceolate to oval leaves smelling strongly of mint. Dense inflorescences of pink or white flowers.
HABITAT: very common in the lower zone and lower forest margins. 150 to 1.000 m.
COMMENTS: Canary endemic with great medicinal value.
CONSERVATION STATUS: LR

BALM OF GILHEAD
Cedronella canariensis (L.) Webb & Berth.

SIZE: grows to 150 cm.
DESCRIPTION: herbaceous with a woody base. Trifoliate perfumed leaves. Pink flowers in terminal heads.
HABITAT: laurel and fayal-brezal forests. Very common between 500 and 1.500 m.
COMMENTS: medicinal, Canary endemic.
CONSERVATION STATUS: LR

CANARY ISLANDS LAVENDER
Lavandula canariensis (L.) Mill.

SIZE: up to 150 cm.
DESCRIPTION: bipinnate shrub. I0 cm. inflorescence spikes. Bluish flowers.
HABITAT: common in the low coastal north, on cliffs and in tabaibales, etc. up to 500 m.
COMMENTS: medicinal, Canary endemic.
CONSERVATION STATUS: LR

SCROPHULARIACEAE

CANARY FIGWORT
Scrophularia smithii   Hornem

SIZE: up to 70 cm.
DESCRIPTION: perennial herb, glabrous leaves with indented borders, green to reddish purple corolla.
HABITAT: laurel and fayal-brezal forests. 500 to 1.000 m.
COMMENTS: Canary endemic represented on Gomera by the subspecies *langaeana*.
CONSERVATION STATUS: VU

BROOM TOADFLAX
Kickxia scoparia   (Brouss.) Kunkel & Sunding

SIZE: up to 40 cm.
DESCRIPTION: scarcely branched perennial. Linear leaves. Yellow, spurred flowers.
HABITAT: locally abundant on rocky slopes and dry fields between 500 and 600 m.
COMMENTS: Canary endemic with relatives in North Africa and the Middle East.
CONSERVATION STATUS: LR

GLOBULARIACEAE

CANARY ISLANDS GLOBULARIA
Globularia salicina   Lam.

SIZE: up to 175 cm.
DESCRIPTION: glabrous, lanceolate leaves, auxilliary inflorescences. Light blue flowers in dense heads.
HABITAT: common on dry slopes of the tabaibales and thermophile forests. 200 to 700 m.
COMMENTS: endemic to Madeira and the Canaries.
CONSERVATION STATUS: LR

PLANTAGINACEAE

SHRUBBY PLANTAIN
Plantago arborescens **Poiret**

SIZE: up to 60 cm.
DESCRIPTION: small shrub with acicular leaves. Black seeds.
HABITAT: rocky areas, ledges, paths etc. in thermophile forests. 400 to 800 m.
COMMENTS: Canary endemic with medicinal seeds.
CONSERVATION STATUS: LR

CAPRIFOLIACEAE

CANARY GUELDER ROSE
Viburnum rigidum **Vent.**

SIZE: reaches 5 m.
DESCRIPTION: oval, downy leaves, umbels of white flowers and subglobular black fruit.
HABITAT: forests, especially the Laurisilva. 500 to 1.200 m.
COMMENTS: ornamental, endemic to Macaronesia.
CONSERVATION STATUS: VU

AQUIFOLIACEAE

CANARY HOLLY
Ilex canariensis **Poiret**

SIZE: up to 10 m.
DESCRIPTION: tree with greyish bark, shiny leaves with oval borders and occasionally, spines. White flowers and globular, red fruit.
HABITAT: common in laurel and fayalbrezal forests between 600 and 1.200 m.
COMMENTS: endemic to the Canaries and Madeira.
CONSERVATION STATUS: LR

COMPOSITAE

GOMERA DAISY
Argyranthemum callichrysum Svent.

SIZE: up to 1 m.
DESCRIPTION: long leaves and yellow, white or cream ligules.
HABITAT: between 500 and 1.200 m. Central region, El Cedro, Valle de Hermigua, Roque Cano, Roque de Agando, Tamaguiche, Igualero.
COMMENTS: ornamental value, endemic to the island.
CONSERVATION STATUS: VU

PARIS DAISY
Argyranthemum frutescens (L.) Sch. Bip.

SIZE: shrubs up to 80 cm.
DESCRIPTION: petiolate, rough, succulent, divided leaves up to 8 cm. Flowers white with a yellow centre.
HABITAT: sea level to 700 m.
COMMENTS: has medicinal properties. Ornamental.
CONSERVATION STATUS: LR

GOMERAN TANSY
Gonospermum gomerae Bolle

SIZE: up to 1 m.
DESCRIPTION: bipinnate leaves, corymbs of yellow flowers.
HABITAT: from 50 to 500 m., between the barrancos of Agulo and Vallehermoso.
COMMENTS: Endemic to the island.
CONSERVATION STATUS: VU

COMPOSITAE (cont.)

VALLEHERMOSO GROUNDSEL
Senecio hermosae Pitard

SIZE: up to 1 m.
DESCRIPTION: trilobate, linear, fleshy leaves. Dense, corymbose inflorescences.
HABITAT: Vallehermoso, cliffs close to Roque Cano, Roque Agando.
COMMENTS: very rare local endemic.
CONSERVATION STATUS: CR

CANARY CANDLE PLANT
Senecio kleinia (L.) Less.

SIZE: up to 2 m.
DESCRIPTION: succulent, glaucous stems and pointed, fleshy, lanceolate, leaves. Umbelliferous inflorescences. Long and thin, pale yellow flowerheads.
HABITAT: common in the low zone. 550 to 1000 m.
COMMENTS: the sap is used locally to clean and disinfect superficial wounds.
CONSERVATION STATUS: LR

GOMERAN CINERARIA
Pericallis steetzii (Bolle) Nord.

SIZE: perrenial up to 45 cm.
DESCRIPTION: inflorescences arranged in dense corymbs of 7 to 25 small (7 mm.) flowerheads.
HABITAT: forests between Roque Agando and El Cedro, Vallehermoso between Epina and Arure. 600 to 1.200 m.
COMMENTS: exclusively on La Gomera.
CONSERVATION STATUS: LR

COMPOSITAE (cont.)

GOMERA MAYFLOWER
Pericallis hansenii Kunkel

SIZE: shrub up to 1.5 m.
DESCRIPTION: glabrous leaves. Stems and petioles covered in white pubescence.
HABITAT: Laurisilva close to the Monte Megida zone, up to 1.000 m.
COMMENTS: La Gomera only.
CONSERVATION STATUS:CR

GOMERA KNAPWEED
Cheirolophus ghomerythus Svent.

SIZE: grows to 1 m.
DESCRIPTION: abundantly bran-ched, violet-pink flowerheads on long stalks.
HABITAT: northern sector, between 5 and 400 m.
COMMENTS: La Gomera only.
CONSERVATION STATUS: CR

ARGAGA KNAPWEED
Cheirolophus sataratensis Svent.

SIZE: up to 1.5 m.
DESCRIPTION: basal branching and abundant, cream-white flowers.
HABITAT: sunny, southern slopes and rugged partially shaded areas. 300 to 600 m.
COMMENTS: Exclusive to La Gomera.
CONSERVATION STATUS: CR

CANARY WORMWOOD
Artemisia canariensis Less.

SIZE: grey shrub up to 1 m.
DESCRIPTION: silver-grey, lobulate leaves with strong odour. Dense inflorescences with golden or dull yellow flowerheads.
HABITAT: low, dry zone, between 50 and 700 m.
COMMENTS: used in an infusion as a good cure for worms, flatulance and stomach pains.
CONSERVATION STATUS: LR

CANARY MOUSE-EAR
Andryala pinnatifida Aiton

SIZE: perennial herb reaching 50 cm.
DESCRIPTION: lanceolate or oval leaves. Dense inflorescences of up to 20 yellow flowers.
HABITAT: common in laurel forests and open areas.
COMMENTS: highly variable Canary endemic.
CONSERVATION STATUS: LR

WALL LETTUCE
Tolpis proustii   Pitard

SIZE: up to 60 cm.
DESCRIPTION: rosettes of leaves some 10 cm. long with stems and petioles covered in white fluff.
HABITAT: Barranco de la Laja, Roque de Agando, Baranquillos de Vallehermoso, Monteforte, etc. Up to 1.000 m.
COMMENTS: found only on La Gomera and El Hierro.
CONSERVATION STATUS: LR

ORTUÑO'S SOW-THISTLE
Sonchus ortunoi   Svent.

SIZE: robust shrub up to 1 m.
DESCRIPTION: leaf rosettes on the stem tips. Sub-corymbose inflorescences with few, (4 to 5 cm. wide), flowerheads.
HABITAT: central and south eastern regions, El Cedro, Valle Gran Rey. North coast, Barranco de Vallehermoso, Roque Cano. Between 200 and 1.000 m.
COMMENTS: endemic to the island.
CONSERVATION STATUS: VU

GOMERA SOW-THISTLE
Sonchus gonzalez-padroni   Svent.

SIZE: up to 80 cm.
DESCRIPTION: basal rosettes of pinnate leaves, inflorescences of 10 tomentose flowerheads.
HABITAT: North coast, Barranco de La Villa to Vallehermoso, Roque Cano. South eastern region, Epina, Arure, Valle Gran Rey, Argaga, etc. 400 and 1.200 m.
COMMENTS: La Gomera only.
CONSERVATION STATUS: VU

FENNEL-LEAVED SOW-THISTLE
Sonchus filifolius   Svent.

SIZE: shrub up to 1.5 m.
DESCRIPTION: leaves long, lobes very slender, few, glabrous. Flowerheads small and slender.
HABITAT: west and southwest of the island, Epina, Lomo Carretón, Valle Gran Rey etc.
COMMENTS: endemic to La Gomera.
CONSERVATION STATE: LR

COMPOSITAE (cont.)

VALLEHERMOSO SOW-THISTLE
Sonchus regis-jubae Pitard

SIZE: shrub, reaching 1.5 m.
DESCRIPTION: leaves in rosettes at the stem tips, flat, linear foliage, lobules, up to 8 cm. wide. Inflorescences in corymbs.
HABITAT: roadsides and cliffs from Barranco de La Villa to Vallehermoso, Riscos de Agulo, Roque Cano. 200 to 600 m.
COMMENTS: endemic to the island.
CONSERVATION STATUS: VU

WILDPRET'S SOWTHISTLE
Sonchus wildpretii U. & A. Reifen

SIZE: shrub, up to 2 m.
DESCRIPTION: large, dense inflorescences, flowerheads with 48 to 62 floscules. Leaves pinnatisect, in terminal groups.
HABITAT: wet cliffs of the north and centre, Los Roques. UP to 1.000m.
COMMENTS: Exclusive to La Gomera.
CONSERVATION STATUS: CR

LILIACEAE

CANARY SMILAX
Smilax canariensis Willd.

SIZE: woody liana up to 2 m. long.
DESCRIPTION: lower stems spiny. Oval leaves cunieform or truncated at the base, borders spineless. Reddish fruit and flowers in umbels.
HABITAT: humid areas. Arure, Chorros de Epina, in and below the Laurisilva. 400 to 1.300 m.
COMMENTS: infusion of the fresh roots and leaves used as a diuretic, to reduce blood glucose, etc.
CONSERVATION STATUS: LR

LILIACEAE (cont.)

UMBELLATE ASPARAGUS
Asparagus umbellatus Link

SIZE: creeping shrub up to 3 m.
DESCRIPTION: smooth stems and simple inflorescences , pendulous and umbellate.
HABITAT:north coast, Agulo, Roque Cano de Vallehermoso.
COMMENTS: rhizomes and stems used as an infusion for their supposed diuretic effects.
CONSERVATION STATUS: LR

CLIMBING BUTCHER'S BROOM
Semele androgyna (L.) Kunth.

SIZE: climbs to 10 m.
DESCRIPTION: cladodes glabrous, lanceolate to oval. Inflorescences at the borders or towards the centres of the undersides of the cladodes. Flowers small, white.
HABITAT: forest areas, El Cedro, Arure, Riscos de Agulo, etc.
COMMENTS: leaves and stems used as a diuretic.
CONSERVATION STATUS: VU

GRAMINEAE

CANARY FALSE BROME
Brachypodium arbusculum Gay ex Knoche

SIZE: perennial up to 60 cm.
DESCRIPTION: rigid, flat or rolled leaves. Erect inflorescences with large lateral spikelets.
HABITAT: cliffs and slopes of the low zone and north coast. Common in the Barranco de La Villa, Agulo, Vallehermoso, Roque Cano, up to 500 m.
COMMENTS: sometimes used as fodder.
CONSERVATION STATUS: LR

GRAMINEAE (cont.)

CANARY FESCUE
Festuca agostinii   Lindinger

SIZE: up to 50 cm.
DESCRIPTION: robust perennial with erect, convoluted leaves and flowers in spikelets.
HABITAT: humid slopes above 600 m. Roque de Agando.
COMMENTS: Canarian endemic, good for fodder.
CONSERVATION STATUS: LR

PALMAE

PALMAE CANARY DATE PALM
Phoenix canariensis   Chabaud

SIZE: up to 18 m.
DESCRIPTION: terminal rosette of up to 200 pinnate, green leaves on a single erect trunk. Elliptical fruit 2 cm. long.
HABITAT: in the low zone, beds of barrancos, slopes with springs, etc. Forms large palm groves. Sea-level up to 1.600 m.
COMMENTS: Canarian endemic used worldwide as a garden plant.
CONSERVATION STATUS: LR

ORCHIDACEAE

CANARY TWAYBLADE
Habenaria tridactylites   Lindl.

SIZE: up to 15 cm.
DESCRIPTION: herbaceous. Two basal, green leaves and a leafless flower stalk. Flowers with a helmet shaped top and three inferior, linear, green lobules
HABITAT: cliffs, paths, etc., of the fayal-brezal and laurel forests. Humid, shaded areas of the thermophile forest.
COMMENTS: Canarian endemic.
CONSERVATION STATUS: LR

FAUNA

MARINE INVERTEBRATES

The rich marine environment of the Islands is home to a large number of invertebrates from many different groups.

The sponges or Porifera are very primitive animals which live by filtering water through their pores. Many of them are vividly coloured and very variable in form.

The echinoderms (starfish, sea urchins etc.) constitute one of the most spectacular groups amongst the marine invertebrates. Some live by grazing on algae and small sedentary animals whilst others are active predators of marine molluscs.

The molluscs form a large group adapted to both terrestrial and aquatic life. The group is represented in the Canaries by four main classes: Gasteropods (snails and sea-slugs) Placophores (chitons), Bivalves (cockles and clams etc.) and Cephalopods (octopus, cuttlefish and squid).

The Annelid or segmented worms can be swimmers such as the polycheates or bristle worms, or sedentary (tube worms). These last-named make a permanent calcareous tube which fixes them to the substrate.

Amongst the Phylum or group of the Cnidarians or coelentrates there are two subdivisions, the Medusozoa or jellyfish and the Anthozoa (sea anemones and corals).

The crustaceans form a group which is fundamentally marine and is represented in the Islands by four types, the Cirripedes or barnacles, the Stomopods (*Squilla mantis*), Isopods or sea-slaters and the Decapods (shrimps, lobsters and crabs).

BREAD-CRUMB SPONGE
Chondrosia reniformis   Nardo

HABITAT: on and amongst rocks in rockpools and shallow water.
COMMENTS: a rubbery, oval or lobular species. Brownish grey with dark patches.

YELLOW FINGERS
Verongia aerophoba   Schmidt

HABITAT: inter-tidal and littoral. In crevices and on rocks with low light intensity down to 20 m.
COMMENTS: resembles a bright yellow hand.

ENCRUSTING SPONGE
Hemimycale columella   Bowerbank

HABITAT: encrusted on rocks of the infralittoral zone at depths between 5 and 25 m.
COMMENTS: varies in colour from pale brick red to pink.

SCARLET STARFISH
Echinaster sepositus Rets.

HABITAT: on rocks and sand of the infralittoral zone, down to 10 m.
COMMENTS: brick red. Can span up to 20 cm.

CANARY STARFISH
Narcissia canariensis D'Orbigny

HABITAT: on rocks of the deep infralittoral and circalittoral zones. To depths of 15 m.
COMMENTS: bright red, reaching a diameter of 30 cm.

SNAKE STARFISH
Ophidiaster ophidianus Lamarck

HABITAT: rockpools and the infralittoral zone down to 15 m.
COMMENTS: can be red, purple or crimson, occasionally a mixture of all three.

RED STARFISH
Hacelia attenuata   Gray

HABITAT: caves of the infralittoral down to 10 m.
COMMENTS: orange-red, reaching 25 cm. in diameter.

STRIPED STARFISH
Coccinasterias tenuispina   Lam.

HABITAT: inter-tidal pools. Has been found as deep as 250 m.
COMMENTS: coloured with brown, greyish brown and blue patches. Grows to 15 cm. in diameter. Preys on invertebrates.

SPINY STARFISH
Marthasterias glacialis   L.

HABITAT: from the inter-tidal zone down to 100 m.
COMMENTS: feeds on sea urchins and molluscs. The largest Canarian starfish, reaching diameters of up to 60 cm.

STARFISH

CUSHION STAR
Asterina gibbosa Penn.

HABITAT: in the inter-tidal zone and under stones on rocky beaches. Can live at depths of up to 100 m.
COMMENTS: brownish coloured. A maximum 5 cm. diameter makes this the smallest Canarian starfish.

BRITTLE STARS

BRITTLE STAR
Ophiotrix fragilis Abildg.

HABITAT: weed encrusted rocks and sand of the infralittoral and circalittoral zones to a depth of 500 m.
COMMENTS: arms up to 12 cm. long. Feeds on small invertebrates.

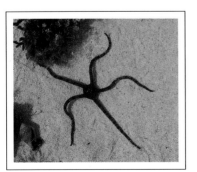

SLENDER BRITTLE STAR
Ophioderma longicaudum Retz.

HABITAT: found in the inter-tidal, infralittoral and circalittoral zones down to 70 m.
COMMENTS: has very flexible arms and can move surprisingly fast. Can grow up to 30 cm. across but most are smaller, at around 15 cm.

CRINOIDS

FEATHER STAR
Antedon bifida   Pennat

HABITAT: infralittoral and circalittoral zones, down to 85 m. Prefers dark environments.
COMMENTS: while the juveniles are sedentary, the adults are able to move around. Rarely grows larger than 10 cm.

SEA CUCUMBERS

COTTON SPINNER
Holothuria sanctori   D. Ch.

HABITAT: in inter-tidal pools and on rocks in less than 20 m. of water.
COMMENTS: feeds on detritus. Grows up to 25 cm. long

SPINY SEA CUCUMBER
Holothuria arguinensis   K. & V.

HABITAT: rockpools and the infralittoral zone.
COMMENTS: feeds on detritus, swallowing sand and weed. Reaches lengths of 20 cm.

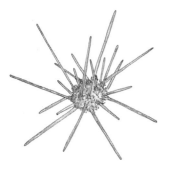

SPINY URCHIN
Cidaris cidaris   L.

HABITAT: buried in sand and mud between 50 and 200 m.
COMMENTS: grows to 10 cm. Rare.

PURPLE SEA URCHIN
Sphaerechinus granularis   Lam.

HABITAT: from the inter-tidal zone down to 100 m.
COMMENTS: consumes algae and detritus. Camouflages itself with shells, pebbles and seaweed held by small suckers. Can reach 13 cm. in diameter.

HEART URCHIN
Brissus unicolor   Leska

HABITAT: at depths between 5 and 25 m.
COMMENTS: feeds on small molluscs, annelid worms and other benthic invertebrates. Up to 15 cm. long.

SEA URCHINS (CONT).

LONG-SPINE BLACK URCHIN
Diadema antillarum   Phillipi

HABITAT: in sometimes very large colonies on infralittoral rocks.
COMMENTS: voracious. Responsible for denuding rocks of all other organisms, leaving bare, white patches.

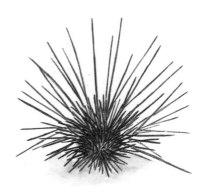

LYRE URCHIN
Plagiobrixsus costai   Gascon

HABITAT: lives buried in the sand at depths between 20 and 150 m.
COMMENTS: feeds on small molluscs and crustaceans. Grows to 10 cm.

MOLLUSCS

GASTEROPODS

ROCK SHELL
Thais haemastoma   L.

SIZE: up to 8 cm.
HABITAT: on rocks of the intertidal and infralittoral zones.
COMMENTS: one of the most common Canarian molluscs.

GASTEROPODS (CONT).

RUSTIC DOVE SHELL
Columbella rustica rustica   Duclos

SIZE: up to 2 cm.
HABITAT: on rocks and under stones of the intertidal and infralittoral zones.
COMMENTS: grazes on algae. Very variable

TRITON SHELL
Charonia tritonis variegata   Lamarck

SIZE: reaches 38 cm.
HABITAT: rocky substrates of the infralittoral and circalittoral zones.
COMMENTS: feeds on algae and detritus.

COMMON CERINTH
Cerithium vulgatum   Bruguiere

SIZE: up to 6 cm.
HABITAT: common in the inter-tidal zone.
COMMENTS: feeds on algae and detritus.

GASTEROPODS (CONT).

TOPSHELL
Osilinus atratus Wood

SIZE: up to 2.5 cm.
HABITAT: on boulders of the intertidal
zone. Common at barranco mouths.
COMMENTS: feeds on algae.

WENDLETRAP
Clathrus clathrus L.

SIZE: up to 2 cm.
HABITAT: rocks, mud and sand from
the low intertidal zone down to 75 m.
COMMENTS: grazes on algae.

PERIWINKLE
Littorina striata King & Broderip

SIZE: up to 1 cm.
HABITAT: supralittoral and high inter-
tidal zones.
COMMENTS: can live for long periods
out of the water.

GASTEROPODS (CONT).

ROUGH STAR SHELL
Astraea rugosa L.

SIZE: up to 5 cm.
HABITAT: lives in the infralittoral and circalittoral zones.
COMMENTS: rare. Has an orange operculum.

LIMPET
Patella piperata Gould.

SIZE: up to 8.5 cm. across.
HABITAT: on rocks in the high inter-tidal zone.
COMMENTS: rare around the western islands.

COWRIE SHELL
Erosaria spurca L.

SIZE: up to 3 cm.
HABITAT: under stones on rocky infra-littoral bottoms.
COMMENTS: probably omnivorous.

GASTEROPODS (CONT).

FEATHERY SEA SLUG
Spurila neapolitana   Delle Chiaje

SIZE: up to 4 cm. long.
HABITAT: amongst algae of the inter-
tidal zone.
COMMENTS: feeds on sea anenomes.

BLUE SEA SLUG
Hypselodoris webbii   D'Orbigny

SIZE: up to 10 cm. long.
HABITAT: in rockpools and under sto-
nes of the infralittoral zone.
COMMENTS: feeds on sponges.

PELAGIC SEA SLUG
Glaucus atlanticus   Foster

SIZE: up to 5 cm. long.
HABITAT: oceanic pelagic.
COMMENTS: feeds on jellyfish, absor-
bing their poisons for its own defense.

SEA HARE
Aplysia dactylomela   Rang

SIZE: as long as 30 cm.
HABITAT: rockpools and the infralittoral zone.
COMMENTS: feeds on algae

BLACK SEA HARE
Aplysia punctata   Cuvier

SIZE: up to 25 cm. long.
HABITAT: infralittoral and inter-tidal zones.
COMMENTS: greyish brown with pale patches.

UMBRELLA LIMPET
Umbraculum mediterraneum   Lamarck

SIZE: up to a diameter of 20 cm.
HABITAT: weedy sand bottoms of the infalittoral zone.
COMMENTS: feeds on sponges.

GASTEROPODS (CONT).

CANARY ISLANDS ORMER
Haliotis coccinea canariensis F. Nordsieck

SIZE: up to 7 cm. long.
HABITAT: shallow infralittoral zone.
COMMENTS: feeds on algae.

PLACOPHORA

CHITON, COAT OF MAIL SHELL
Chiton canariensis D'Orbigny

SIZE: up to 4 cm.
HABITAT: under stones in the inter-
tidal and shallow infralittoral zones.
COMMENTS: usually a greenish-
brown colour.

BIVALVES

BROWN VENUS
Callista chione L.

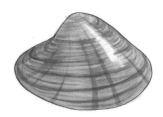

SIZE: up to 8 cm. across.
HABITAT: under sand and mud in shallow waters.
COMMENTS: the shell is yellowish and
covered with concentric brown lines.

BIVALVES (CONT.)

WARTY VENUS
Venus verrucosa L.

SIZE: up to 6 cm.
HABITAT: sandy and weedy bottoms from the infralittoral zone down to 100m.
COMMENTS: shell is greyish-yellow with brown patches. Edible.

MUSSEL
Perna perna L.

SIZE: up to 9 cm. long.
HABITAT: on low intertidal and infralittoral rocks on rough coasts.
COMMENTS: edible.

SADDLE OYSTER
Anomia ephippium L.

SIZE: up to 6 cm.
HABITAT: hard substrates from the inter-tidal to the circalittoral zone.
COMMENTS: the shell is often covered with cirripedes, sponges, calcareous algae, etc.

CUTTLEFISH
Sepia officinalis   L.

SIZE: up to 40 cm.
HABITAT: sandy infralittoral zone, sometimes venturing much deeper.
COMMENTS: feeds on fish and crustaceans. Can weigh as much as 3.5 kg.

COMMON OCTOPUS
Octopus vulgaris   Lamarck

SIZE: up to 1 m.
HABITAT: rocky infralittoral zone, hiding in caves during the day. Small examples are sometimes found in rockpools.
COMMENTS: can change colour to match the backround. Large examples(over 1 m. long) can weigh up to 8 kg.

LONG-FINNED SQUID
Loligo vulgaris   Lamarck

SIZE: up to 50 cm.
HABITAT: oceanic pelagic. Comes closer to shore to spawn.
COMMENTS: feeds on fish.

CEPHALOPODS (CONT).

Serpula vermicularis   **L.**

SIZE: up to 10 cm.
HABITAT: shallow infralittoral and circalittoral zones.
COMMENTS: makes and lives in a cylindrical tube.

RAGWORM
Hermodice carunculata   **Pallas**

SIZE: up to 40 cm. long.
HABITAT: intertidal to circalittoral zones.
COMMENTS: the bristles along its flanks come off easily, causing skin irritation.

MARINE INVERTEBRATES - CNIDARIA

PORTUGUESE MAN-O-WAR
Physalia physalis   **L.**

SIZE: 30 cm. long by 10 cm. wide.
HABITAT: open ocean. Sometimes washed or blown to the coast.
COMMENTS: a colony or organisms making up a bluish air-sack and long stinging tentacles. Its sting causes serious skin burns.

CNIDARIA (CONT).

PHOSPHORESCENT JELLYFISH
Pelagia noctiluca   Forskal

SIZE: reaches diameters of 10 cm.
HABITAT: pelagic.
COMMENTS: moves by contracting its umbrella. Luminescent. One of the easiest species to see in the islands.

BY-THE WIND SAILOR
Velella velella   L.

SIZE: up to 8 cm. across.
HABITAT: pelagic.
COMMENTS: bluish, oval, with a transparent sail. Sporadic in Canary waters.

OPALET SEA ANEMONE
Anemonia sulcata   Pennant

SIZE: 7 cm. wide, 10 cm. tall.
HABITAT: on rocky substrates of the intertidal and occasionally the shallow infralittoral zones.
COMMENTS: the most common ane-mone.

STALKED SEA ANEMONE
Aiptasia mutabilis   Gravenhorst

SIZE: up to 20 cm. tall.
HABITAT: on rocky and mixed bottoms in the inter-tidal and infralittoral zones.
COMMENTS: possesses over 100 tentacles arranged in an oral disc.

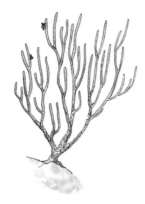

HORN CORAL
Lophogorgia viminalis   Pallas

SIZE: up to 80 cm. tall.
HABITAT: deep infralittoral zone from 15 m. down to the circalittoral zone.
COMMENTS: varies from orange yellow to purple.

RED HORN CORAL
Lophogorgia ruberrima   Koch

SIZE: up to 30 cm. tall.
HABITAT: from depths of 15 m. down to the circalittoral zone.
COMMENTS: coral-red.

FEATHER CORAL
Aglaophenia pluma **L.**

SIZE: up to 7 cm. tall.
HABITAT: intertidal and infralittoral zones.
COMMENTS: feathery colonial species. Grows on seaweed, shells and rocks.

CORAL
Dendrophyllia ramea **L.**

SIZE: up to 1 m. tall.
HABITAT: in waters deeper than 45 m.
COMMENTS: colonial species. Polyps have orange centres and white tentacles.

JEWEL ANEMONE
Corynactis viridis **Allman**

SIZE: up to 5 mm. In diameter.
HABITAT: vertical walls from the lower limits of the inter-tidal zone down to 20 m.
COMMENTS: solitary polyp with over 100 tentacles. Colour varies greatly.

STAR CORAL
Balanophyllia regia   Gosse

SIZE: up to 1 cm.
HABITAT: vertical rock walls from the lower limits of the inter-tidal zone down to 20 m.
COMMENTS: a solitary, reddish-orange species.

MARINE INVERTEBRATES - CHORDATES

SEA SQUIRTS

SEA SQUIRT
Ascidia mentula   Muller

SIZE: up to 20 cm.
HABITAT: fixed to rocks, under stones, in caves, etc. Lower inter-tidal down to the bathylittoral zone (250 m.).
COMMENTS: Solitary. A light, transparent green.

ERECT SEA SQUIRT
Ciona intestinalis   L.

SIZE: up to 15 cm. long.
HABITAT: on rocks, under stones, in caves, etc. Lower inter-tidal zone down to 250 m.
COMMENTS: yellowish   green. Solitary.

SEA SQUIRTS (CONT.)

RED SEA SQUIRT
Halocynthia papillosa   **L.**

SIZE: up to 7 cm.
HABITAT: stuck to rocks, under stones, in caves, etc. Infralittoral and circalittoral zones.
COMMENTS: solitary. Intense red above and reddish yellow underneath.

MARINE INVERTEBRATES - ARTHROPODS

CRUSTACEANS

ACORN BARNACLE
Chthamalus stellatus   **Poli**

SIZE: up to 8 mm. In diameter.
HABITAT: rocks and boulders of the upper inter-tidal zone.
COMMENTS: greyish-yellow.

GOOSE BARNACLE
Lepas anatifera   **L.**

SIZE: up to 8 cm.
HABITAT: stuck to floating oceanic debris.
COMMENTS: forms bunch-like colonies.

SEA SLATER
Ligia italica   Fabricius

SIZE: up to 12 mm.
HABITAT: rocks and boulders of the supralittoral zone.
COMMENTS: brownish grey with grey or greenish speckles.

SNAPPING PRAWN
Alpheus dentipes   Guerin

SIZE: up to 2 cm.
HABITAT: rockpools down to 100 m.
COMMENTS: olive green. Its name comes from the sound made by its large pincer, used to scare predators and stun prey.

ELEGANT PRAWN
Gnatophyllum elegans   Risso

SIZE: up to 4 cm.
HABITAT: inter-tidal zone down to 10 m.
COMMENTS: appendages and tail are transluscent purple. Body is brown with yellow spots.

CRUSTACEANS (CONT.)

PINK SHRIMP
Plesionika edwardsii Brandt

SIZE: up to 17 cm.
HABITAT: down to depths of 650 m.
COMMENTS: common. Excellent eating, much appreciated in the islands.

PRAWN
Palaemon elegans Rathke

SIZE: up to 5 cm.
HABITAT: rock pools.
COMMENTS: transluscent. Good bait for sea bream.

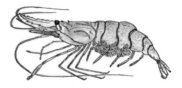

LOCUST LOBSTER
Scyllarides latus Latreille

SIZE: up to 50 cm.
HABITAT: infralittoral seabed down to 25 m.
COMMENTS: eats molluscs buried in the mud.

CRUSTACEANS (CONT.)

LARGE HERMIT CRAB
Dardanus callidus   Risso

SIZE: up to 5 cm.
HABITAT: to depths of 50 m.
COMMENTS: symbiotic with the ane-
mone *Calliactis parasitica*.

BLUE-CLAWED HERMIT CRAB
Clibanarius aequabilis   Dana

SIZE: up to 1 cm.
HABITAT: between 5 and 20 m. of
water.
COMMENTS: recognised by its blue
and red markings.

COMMON HERMIT CRAB
Pagurus anachoretus   Risso

SIZE: up to 25 mm.
HABITAT: from 5 to 25 m. of water.
COMMENTS: generally bright red or
yellow.

SPIDER CRAB
Paromola cuvieri Risso

SIZE: up to 22 cm.
HABITAT: circalittoral seabed down to 650 m.
COMMENTS: a uniform reddish colour.

LEOPARD CRAB
Calappa granulata L.

SIZE: up to 10 cm. across.
HABITAT: buried in sand of the deep infralittoral and circalittoral zones.
COMMENTS: carapace has red patches on a yellowish grey backround.

TOOTHED ROCK CRAB
Cancer bellianus Johnson

SIZE: 14 by 20 cm.
HABITAT: common deeper than 200 m.
COMMENTS: reddish-yellow with black pincers.

STONE CRAB
Xantho poressa   Olivi

SIZE: 4 by 2.5 cm.
HABITAT: intertidal rock pools.
COMMENTS: used on some islands as bait for parrotfish (*Sparisoma cretense* L.).

LIGHTFOOT CRAB
Grapsus grapsus   L.

SIZE: carapace up to 10 cm.
HABITAT: high intertidal and supralit-toral zones.
COMMENTS: reddish black.

MARBLED CRAB
Pachygrapsus marmoratus fabricius

SIZE: up to 3.5 cm.
HABITAT: intertidal and shallow infra-littoral zones.
COMMENTS: dark, greenish brown with lighter lines and spots.

CRUSTACEANS (CONT.)

ROCK CRAB
*Plagusia depress*a   Fabricius

SIZE: carapace up to 5 cm. across.
HABITAT: rocky substrates on very rough coasts.
COMMENTS: darkish red. Known in some areas as the red crab.

BANDED SPIDER CRAB
Percnon gibbesi   A. Milne Edwards

SIZE: carapace 2.5 cm. across.
HABITAT: rock pools down to 25 m.
COMMENTS: brown or orange with flourescent green lines.

SPINY SPIDER CRAB
Maja squinado   Herbst.

SIZE: up to 20 cm. across.
HABITAT: rocky, infralittoral bottoms down to 50 m.
COMMENTS: reddish to pinkish-white.

CRUSTACEANS (CONT.)

LONG-LEGGED SPIDER CRAB
Stenorhynchus lanceolatus Brullé

SIZE: carapace 2 cm. across.
HABITAT: rocky infralittoral and circalittoral zones down to 100 m.
COMMENTS: reddish, with clear
bands on the carapace.

PORCELAIN CRAB
Porcelana platycheles Pennant

SIZE: up to 15 mm.
HABITAT: under stones in the inter-
tidal zone.
COMMENTS: covered in dense greyish pubescence.

TERRESTRIAL MOLLUSCS

GARDEN SNAIL
Helix aspersa   Müll

HABITAT: common in humid areas; gardens, forests, etc.
COMMENTS: an Eastern European and Mediterranean species.

DUNE SNAIL
Theba pisana   Müll

HABITAT: common in dry zones, low or coastal land, dunes, etc. Often found on plant leaves and stems.
COMMENTS: an African and North Mediterranean species.

TRUNCATED DOOR SNAIL
Rumina decollata   L.

HABITAT: locally abundant on dry and especially chalky soils.
COMMENTS: the adult shell is truncated.

WOODLAND SNAIL
Napaeus variatus   Web & Berth.

HABITAT: dense vegetation of the low and forest zones.
COMMENTS: an endemic exclusive to La Gomera.

MEDITERRANEAN SNAIL
Helicella apicina   Lmk.

HABITAT: under stones and on cultivated land in humid areas.
COMMENTS: Mediterranean species.

EDIBLE SNAIL
Otala lactea   Müll.

HABITAT: humid   areas;   gardens,
farmland and forests.
COMMENTS: an edible species from
the Mediterranean.

SLUG
Limax flavus   L.

HABITAT: associated with man; gardens and farmland.
COMMENTS: large species, reaching
lengths of over 10 cm.

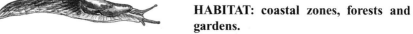

BLACK SLUG
Milax gagates   Draparmaud

HABITAT: coastal zones, forests and
gardens.
COMMENTS: a European species.

The aracnids of the Canary Islands are one of the least studied groups of animals. There are probably between 120 and 150 species of spiders on the islands, a large number of which are also found in Europe and the Mediterranean region. Others are of tropical or subtropical origin.

The class Aracnida is made up of 10 orders, including spiders, palpograds, scorpions, pseudoscorpions, harvestmen and mites.

On the island of La Gomera continental species such as *Eresus niger* from Europe, *Arctosa cinerea* from the Mediterranean region and *Agelenia canariensis* from North Africa are common.

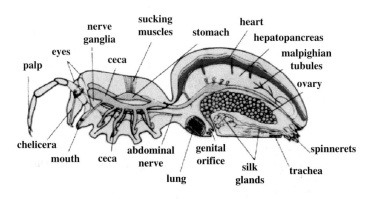

Anatomy of a spider

SHEEP TICK
Ixodes trilineatu   Lucas

SIZE: up to 11 mm.
HABITAT: the larva live amongst dry vegetation while the adults stick to mammals (goats, sheep, dogs, humans, etc.), feeding on their blood.
COMMENTS: a widespread, almost cosmopolitan species.

HARVESTMAN
Pholcus phalangioides   Fuessl.

SIZE: up to 2 cm.
HABITAT: lives in untidy webs placed in the corners of buildings, barns and houses.
COMMENTS: present in all subtropical areas.

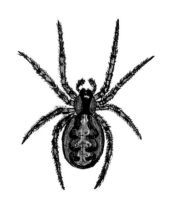

ORB-WEB SPIDER
Zygiella x - notata   Cl.

SIZE: reaches 6 mm.
HABITAT: found mostly in houses, on window frames, etc.
COMMENTS: common European species with a characteristic web.

Heterodyctina puella Simon

SIZE: up to 3 mm.
HABITAT: gardens and humid areas.
COMMENTS: locally frequent. Also found on Gran Canaria and Tenerife

Pisaura mirabilis Cl.

SIZE: as long as 1.5 cm.
HABITAT: forests.
COMMENTS: found on the central and western islands.

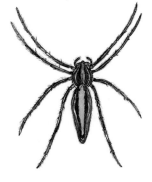

WOLF SPIDER
Arctosa cinerea F.

SIZE: up to 1.6 cm.
HABITAT: humid areas, in burrows and under stones.
COMMENTS: North African and Mediterranean species, feeding on small insects. Also found on Gran Canaria, Fuerteventura and Tenerife.

BLACK WIDOW
Latrodectus mactans   Fabricius

SIZE: up to 1 cm.
HABITAT: dry, sandy areas.
COMMENTS: feeds on small invertebrates. Female often eats the male after copulation.

PRICKLY PEAR SPIDER
Cyrtophora citricola   Forsk.

SIZE: up to 9 mm.
HABITAT: low zone, in century plants and prickly pears.
COMMENTS: common, colonial species forming large, irregular webs. One of the commonest spiders of the archipelago, found on all seven islands.

TUBE WEB SPIDER
Agelena canariensis   Lucas

SIZE: reaches 9 mm.
HABITAT: dry areas, amongst vegetation.
COMMENTS: North African species, found on La Gomera, Gran Canaria and Tenerife. Builds an open ended, tubular web.

Steatoda grossa   C.L. Koch

SIZE: up to 1 cm.
HABITAT: houses and buildings.
COMMENTS: on all the islands except
La Palma and Fuerteventura.

HEATH SPIDER
Eresus niger   Pet.

SIZE: reaches 1.2 cm.
HABITAT: vertical, tubular webs in the
soil.
COMMENTS: colonial species present
only on La Gomera.

Dysdera crocata   C.L. Koch

SIZE: up to 1.1 cm.
HABITAT: under stones, feeding on
woodlice.
COMMENTS: nocturnal. Widespread,
almost cosmopolitan. Found on La
Gomera and the central and eastern
islands.

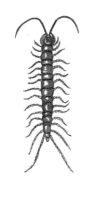

CENTIPEDE
Lithobius forficatus   L.

SIZE: up to 3 cm.
HABITAT: hidden under stones during the day. Comes out at night to hunt small insects.
COMMENTS: a   European   and Mediterranean species of wide distribution.

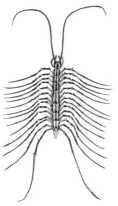

CENTIPEDE
Scutigera coleoptrata   L.

SIZE: up to 7 cm.
HABITAT: live in caves and can be found in houses and buildings.
COMMENTS: active,   fast-running. Mediterranean species which feeds on insects and spiders.

MILLIPEDE
Ommatoiulus moreletii   Lucas.

SIZE: up to 5'5 cm.
HABITAT: In shady places under stones and fallen leaf-litter.
COMMENTS: the most common millipede in the islands. It feeds on detritus.

INSECTS

The insects constitute the most extensive and numerous group in the Animal Kingdom with about 1.000.000 known species.

They also form the group with the most diversity and are distributed throughout the globe in marine, terrestrial, freshwater and airborne habitats.

The insects have an exoskeleton of chitin which covers and protects the body and bits internal organs. They differ from the other arthropods such as the spiders, miriopods or crustaceans as they are the only ones having three pairs of jointed legs.

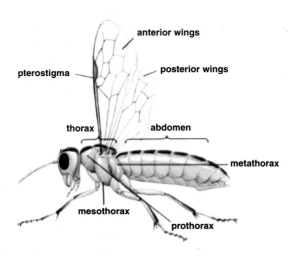

General diagram of an insect

EMPEROR DRAGONFLY
Anax imperator Leach

FAMILY: Aeschinidae
SIZE: up to 8 cm.
HABITAT: still water.
COMMENTS: the female body is
rather greener than the male.

RED DARTER
Crocothemis erythraea Brulle

FAMILY: Libellulidae
SIZE: up to 5 cm.
HABITAT: around still water.
COMMENTS: male bright red, female
yellowish.

BLUE DARTER
Orthetrum chrysostigma Burmeister

FAMILY: Libellulidae
SIZE: up to 5 cm.
HABITAT: near still water.
COMMENTS: rarer than the two pre-
vious species.

ODONATA

YELLOW DARTER
Sympetrum fonscolombei Selys

FAMILY: Libellulidae
SIZE: up to 4 cm.
HABITAT: still water.
COMMENTS: male reddish yellow, female ochre.

AFRICAN DARTER
Zygonix terrida Kirby

FAMILY: Libellulidae
SIZE: up to 6 cm.
HABITAT: close to still water.
COMMENTS: metallic blue and yellow coloration.

ORTHOPTERA

HOUSE CRICKET
Acheta domestica L.

FAMILY: Gryllidae
SIZE: up to 4 cm.
HABITAT: houses, gardens and around rubbish.
COMMENTS: nocturnal species with a loud song, originally from Asia and North Africa.

FIELD CRICKET
Grillus binmaculatus   De Geer

FAMILY: Gryllidae
SIZE: up to 4 cm.
HABITAT: excavates its own holes and burrows.
COMMENTS: the most common cricket on the islands.

MOLE CRICKET
Gryllotalpa africana   Beauvois

FAMILY: Gryllotalpidae
SIZE: up to 3 cm.
HABITAT: humid ground close to water.
COMMENTS: burrowing species which occasionally flies at night.

MEDITERRANEAN BUSH CRICKET
Phaneroptera nana sparsa   Stal.

FAMILY: Tettigoniidae
SIZE: only 2 cm.
HABITAT: dry scrub to farmland.
COMMENTS: nocturnal.

BLUE WING GRASSHOPPER
Oedipoda canariensis   Krauss

FAMILY: Acrididae
SIZE: up to 3 cm.
HABITAT: dry, rocky or sandy areas up to 800 m..
COMMENTS: locally frequent. Also present on Gran Canaria and Tenerife.

CANARY GRASSHOPPER
Sphingonotus willemsei   Misch.

FAMILY: Acrididae
SIZE: small, at 1.5 cm.
HABITAT: dry habitats, semideserts up to 300 m.
COMMENTS: found on all the central and western islands.

EGYPTIAN GRASSHOPPER
Anacridium aegyptium   L.

FAMILY: Cantantopidae
SIZE: up to 1.6 cm.
HABITAT: open habitats, shrubs etc. in warm dry habitats.
COMMENTS: also found on Fuerteventura, Gran Canaria and Tenerife.

GREAT BUSH CRICKET
Calliphona alluaudi   Bolívar

FAMILY: Tettigoniidae
SIZE: up to 3 cm.
HABITAT: on trees and shrubs of forested areas.
COMMENTS: most active just after dusk.

GREY BUSH CRICKET
Platycleis tesellata   Fabricius

FAMILY: Tettigoniidae
SIZE: up to 4 cm.
HABITAT: dry areas.
COMMENTS: also recorded on Gran Canaria and Tenerife.

RED WING GRASSHOPPER
Scintharista notabilis   Walker

FAMILY: Acrididae
SIZE: females up to 3.5 cm., males to 2.5 cm.
HABITAT: arid zones and mountain slopes from sea level to 1.400 m.
COMMENTS: strong flier.

AFRICAN LOCUST
Schistocerca gregaria   Forskal

FAMILY: Acrididae
SIZE: up to 6.5 cm.
HABITAT: cultivated land and dry pla-
ces in the lower zone.
COMMENTS: the main plague species
in Africa.

SAND GRASSHOPPER
Acrotylus insubricus   Scopoli

FAMILY: Acrididae
SIZE: up to 3 cm.
HABITAT: coastal and xerophytic vege-
tation between sea level and 650 m.
Common in sandy areas and dunes.
COMMENTS: Mediterranean species
common in the Canaries.

WINGLESS CRICKET
Acrostyra bellamyi   Uvarov

FAMILY: Pamphagidae
SIZE: females reach 7 cm.
HABITAT: laurel forests.
COMMENTS: wingless endemic,
exclusive to La Gomera.

ORTHOPTERA (CONT.)

COMMON GRASSHOPPER
Calliptamus plebeius   Walker

FAMILY: Acrididae
SIZE: males to 2 cm, females up to 3 cm.
HABITAT: brush and scrub from the coast to 2.000 m.
COMMENTS: highly variable, ever present all over the Canaries.

GREEN GRASSHOPPER
Ailopus thalassinus thalassinus Fabricius

FAMILY: Acrididae
SIZE: males up to 2.5cm, females larger, reaching 3.3 cm.
HABITAT: both wet and dry conditions; forests, scrub and farmland.
COMMENTS: Mediterranean/Southern European species, common on the islands.

DERMAPTERA

GIANT EARWIG
Anisolabis maxima   Brullé

FAMILY: Carciophoridae
SIZE: up to 3.4 cm.
HABITAT: under stones in humid conditions. mid altitude up to the mountains.

DERMAPTERA (CONT.)

EARWIG
Euborellia annulipes   Lucas

FAMILY: Carcinophoridae
SIZE: only 1 cm.
HABITAT: leaf litter and under stones in humid conditions.
COMMENTS: locally frequent, wingless.

EARWIG
Labidura riparia   Pallas

FAMILY: Labiduridae
SIZE: up to 3.6 cm.
HABITAT: sandy sites of the low zone up to the forests.
COMMENTS: cosmopolitan species, excavates burrows in sand.

DICTYOPTERA

AMERICAN COCKROACH
Periplaneta americana   L.

FAMILY: Blattidae
SIZE: up to 4 cm.
HABITAT: houses and refuse in urban areas.
COMMENTS: universally associated with man.

FLYING COCKROACH
Leucophaea maderae   Fabricius

FAMILY: Blattidae
SIZE: reaches 5 cm.
HABITAT: associated with old buildings and abandoned houses.
COMMENTS: the largest Canarian cockroach. Usually associated with man.

PALE MANTIS
Pseudoyersinia pilipes   Chopard

FAMILY: Mantidae
SIZE: males only 2 cm., females up to 3 cm.
HABITAT: vegetation of the low, dry, shrub zone.
COMMENTS: endemic to La Gomera.

SLENDER MANTIS
Hypsicorypha gracilis   Burmeister

FAMILY: Empusidae
SIZE: up to 8 cm.
HABITAT: coastal zones, fields and dry scrub.
COMMENTS: colour varies to match the surroundings.

AFRICAN GROUND BUG
Spilostethus pandurus   Scopoli

FAMILY: Lygacidae
SIZE: up to 1.5 cm.
HABITAT: dry, cultivated areas.
COMMENTS: subtropical species present on all the islands.

BLACK & RED GROUND BUG
Scantius aegyptius   L.

FAMILY: Phyrrhocoridae
SIZE: up to 9 mm.
HABITAT: arid regions.
COMMENTS: colonial, found on all the islands.

BLACK SHIELD BUG
Macroscytus brunneus   Fabricius

FAMILY: Cydnidae
SIZE: up to 1 cm.
HABITAT: low, dry sites and farmland.
COMMENTS: Mediterranean and North African species, common on all the western islands.

PIED SHIELD BUG
Codophila varia   Fabricius

FAMILY: Pentatomidae
SIZE: up to 1.2 cm.
HABITAT: on cultivated land.
COMMENTS: Mediterranean species.

HARLEQUIN BUG
Eurydema ornatum   L.

FAMILY: Pentatomidae
SIZE: up to 8 mm.
HABITAT: on species of the cabbage family in cultivated areas.
COMMENTS: Mediterranean.

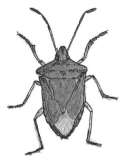

GREEN SHIELD BUG
Nezara viridula   L.

FAMILY: Pentatomidae
SIZE: up to 1.1 cm.
HABITAT: from the coast up to 1.000 m.
COMMENTS: cosmopolitan.

NETTLE BUG
Heterogaster urticae   Fabricius

FAMILY: Lygaeidae
SIZE: up to 7 mm.
HABITAT: forests and farmland.
COMMENTS: feeds on nettle seeds.

CAPSID BUG
Calocoris norvegicus   Gmel.

FAMILY: Miridae
SIZE: only 6 mm.
HABITAT: on weeds and potatoes
COMMENTS: feeds on flowers and buds.

CANARY WATER BOATMAN
Noctonecta canariensis Kirk

FAMILY: Notonectidae
SIZE: up to 1.3 cm.
HABITAT: in pools and water tanks.
COMMENTS: a Canarian endemic.

STINK BUG
Brachypelta aterrima   Forst.

FAMILY: Cydnidae
SIZE: up to 6 mm.
HABITAT: dry areas on a wide variety of plants.
COMMENTS: Mediterranean/European species.

LACE BUG, THISTLE BUG
Tingis cardui   L.

FAMILY: Tingitidae
SIZE: up to 5 mm.
HABITAT: in cultivated areas, on thistles.
COMMENTS: Mediterranean/European species.

BED BUG
Cimex lectularis   L.

FAMILY: Cimicidae
SIZE: only 4 mm.
HABITAT: a cosmopolitan plague found in villages.
COMMENTS: feeds on blood, both animal and human.

HEMIPTERA (CONT.)

WATER MEASURER
Hydrometra stagnorum   L.

FAMILY: Hydrometridae
SIZE: up to 1 cm.
HABITAT: on the surface of freshwater pools.
COMMENTS: feeds on small insects.

POND SKATER
Gerris thoracicus   L.

FAMILY: Gerridae
SIZE: up to 1 cm.
HABITAT: on the surface of pools in forests.
COMMENTS: feeds on small insects.

NEUROPTERA - lacewings

ANT LION
Myrmeleon alternans   Brullé

FAMILY: Myrmeleontidae
SIZE: up to 3 cm.
HABITAT: amongst vegetation.
COMMENTS: larva makes pit traps to catch ants and small insects.

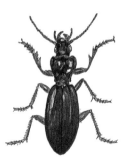

GROUND BEETLE
Broscus crasimargo   Wollaston

FAMILY: Carabidae
SIZE: up to 2.2 cm.
HABITAT: laurel forests, rare in the El Cedro region.
COMMENTS: endemic to La Gomera.

COMMON GROUND BEETLE
Campalita maderae   Fabricius

FAMILY: Carabidae
SIZE: up to 2.7 cm.
HABITAT: from the shoreline to the forests.
COMMENTS: an introduced species.

GREEN GROUND BEETLE
Chlaenius spoliatus   Rossi

FAMILY: Carabidae
SIZE: up to 1.4 cm.
HABITAT: very humid conditions of the low zone such as the borders of aqueducts.
COMMENTS: easily recognised due to its golden wing-case edges.

Cymindis simillina Wollaston

FAMILY: Carabidae
SIZE: up to 12 mm.
HABITAT: from the coast up to 1.000 m.
COMMENTS: endemic to the island.

Harpalus distinguedus Duftschmidt

FAMILY: Carabidae
SIZE: up to 11 mm.
HABITAT: amongst stones of the forests and the low zone.
COMMENTS: shiny green. Locally abundant, especially during the spring.

Agonum nicholsii Fabricius

FAMILY: Carabidae
SIZE: up to 10 mm.
HABITAT: humid conditions.
COMMENTS: endemic to La Gomera.

COLEOPTERA (CONT.) (GROUND BEETLES)

Ocydromus atlanticus   Wollaston

FAMILY: Carabidae
SIZE: only 5 mm.
HABITAT: pond and aqueduct borders from the low zone up to the forests.
COMMENTS: present on all the islands.

Dromius plagipennis   L.

FAMILY: Carabidae
SIZE: only 5 mm.
HABITAT: under bark and in mosses and lichens of Laurisilva trees.
COMMENTS: one of 4 *Dromius* species on the islands.

Trechus flavocintus   Jeann

FAMILY: Carabidae
SIZE: up to 4 mm.
HABITAT: humid, rocky areas in the Laurisilva.
COMMENTS: rare endemic represented on La Gomera by the subspecies *gomerea*.

GREAT DIVING BEETLE
Meladema coriacea   Castelnau

FAMILY: Dystiscidae
SIZE: up to 2 cm.
HABITAT: streams and still water.
COMMENTS: locally abundant. A good flier.

WHIRLIGIG BEETLE
Grynus dejeani   Brullé

FAMILY: Gyrinidae
SIZE: up to 7 mm.
HABITAT: streams and clear water.
COMMENTS: swims in groups, in circles on the water's surface.

SMALL DIVING BEETLE
Hydroporus errans   L.

FAMILY: Dytiscidae
SIZE: up to 3 mm.
HABITAT: still water and pools.
COMMENTS: European species.

WATER BEETLE
Laccobius minutus   Wollaston

FAMILY: Hydrophillidae
SIZE: up to 4.5 mm.
HABITAT: pools, streams and water tanks.
COMMENTS: a European species.

DARK LADYBIRD
Rhyzobius litura   Fabricius

FAMILY: Coccinellidae
SIZE: up to 3 mm.
HABITAT: on bushes feeding on aphids.
COMMENTS: a European species.

7-SPOT LADYBIRD
Coccinelea algerica   Kovar

FAMILY: Coccinellidae
SIZE: up to 8.2 mm.
HABITAT: forests and farmland of the low zone. Feeds on aphids.
COMMENTS: A Canarian endemic

COLEOPTERA (CONT.)

DUNG BEETLE
Hister major   Hoffm.

FAMILY: Histeridae
SIZE: up to 8.5 cm.
HABITAT: in dungheaps up to 300 m.
COMMENTS: feeds on the larva of other insects.

ROVE BEETLE
Creophilus maxillosus   L.

FAMILY: Staphilinidae
SIZE: reaches 2.6 cm.
HABITAT: in dung and rubbish.
COMMENTS: feeds on smaller insects

DEVIL'S COACH HORSE BEETLE
Ocypus olens olens   Müller

FAMILY: Staphylinidae
SIZE: reaches 3 cm.
HABITAT: low and middle zones, under stones, leaves and logs.
COMMENTS: lifts its abdomen mimicking a scorpion when disturbed.

ROVE BEETLE
Habrocerus capillaricornis   Wollaston

FAMILY: Staphylinidae
SIZE: up to 3 mm.
HABITAT: amongst leaf litter in humid forest areas.
COMMENTS: a European species.

DUNG BEETLE
Aphodius hydrochaeris   Fabricius

FAMILY: Scarabaeidae
SIZE: up to 7 mm.
HABITAT: on dung.
COMMENTS: European/Mediterranean.

RHINOCEROS BEETLE
Oryctes nasicornis prolixus   Wollaston

FAMILY: Scarabaeidae
SIZE: reaches 4 cm.
HABITAT: mainly at low altitudes.
COMMENTS: the larva feed on the dead trunks of Canary Palms (*Phoenix canariensis*).

COLEOPTERA (CONT.)

FLOWER CHAFER
Tropinota squalida canariensis Lindberg

FAMILY: Scarabacidae
SIZE: up to 1.2 cm.
HABITAT: pollen feeder present from the coast to the mountains.
COMMENTS: an endemic Canary subspecies.

ROVE BEETLE
Xantholinus punctulatus   Payk.

FAMILY: Staphylinidae
SIZE: up to 8 mm.
HABITAT: plant litter, dung, farmland and forests.
COMMENTS: European species.

BUPRESTID BEETLE
Buprestis bertheloti   Castelnau & Gory

FAMILY: Buprestidae
SIZE: up to 2.5 cm.
HABITAT: Canary Pine (*Pinus canariensis*) forests and plantations.
COMMENTS: endemic to the islands. The larva feeds on dead pine wood.

DARKLING BEETLE
Hegeter tristis   Fabricius

FAMILY: Tenebrionidae
SIZE: up to 1.6 cm.
HABITAT: low altitudes and sandy coasts.
COMMENTS: there are around 20 species of *Hegeter* in the Canaries.

SAND BEETLE
Zophosis bicarinata bicarinata Solieri

FAMILY: Tenebrionidae
SIZE: up to 6.3 mm.
HABITAT: coastal areas, especially on sand and dunes.
COMMENTS: endemic to La Gomera, Gran Canaria and Tenerife.

MEALWORM BEETLE
Tenebrio obscurus   Fabricius

FAMILY: Tenebrionidae
SIZE: up to 1.5 cm.
HABITAT: in rubbish and warehouses.
COMMENTS: larva feeds on flour and grain.

SEAWEED BEETLE
Phaleria cadaverina   Steph.

FAMILY: Tenebrionidae
SIZE: up to 7 mm.
HABITAT: black sand and white chalk
beaches often in seaweed.
COMMENTS: present on La Gomera,
Fuerteventura and Tenerife.

LONG HORN BEETLE
Lepromoris gibba   Brullé

FAMILY: Cerambycidae
SIZE: up to 2.2 cm.
HABITAT: low and mid altitudes on
dead Cardon (*Euphorbia canariensis*)
stems.
COMMENTS: genus endemic to the
Canaries.

OSIER LONGHORN BEETLE
Gracilia minuta   Steph.

FAMILY: Cerambycidae
SIZE: up to 6 mm.
HABITAT: dry *Salix* wood.
COMMENTS: associated with man.

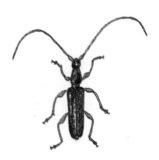

Leptura palmi   L.

FAMILY: Cerambycidae
SIZE: up to 1.7 cm.
HABITAT: the trunks of dead laurel forest trees.
COMMENTS: endemic to the islands.

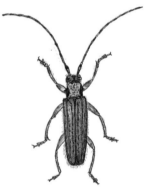

LONGHORN
Stenidea anulicornis   Brullé

FAMILY: Cerambycidae
SIZE: up to 2 cm.
HABITAT: on figs, sorrel, spurges and brambels etc.
COMMENTS: a Canarian endemic.

LADER BEETLE
Carpophilus hemipterus   L.

FAMILY: Nitidulidae
SIZE: only 3 mm.
HABITAT: in food stores.
COMMENTS: almost universal.

COLEOPTERA (CONT.)

POLLEN BEETLE
Meligethes tristis   Schüpp.

FAMILY: Nitidulidae
SIZE: up to 2.5 cm.
HABITAT: on flowers of the cabbage family.
COMMENTS: European species

SAW-TOOTHED GRAIN BEETLE
Oryzaephilus surinamensis   L.

FAMILY: Silvanidae
SIZE: only 3 mm.
HABITAT: found in flour and grain.
COMMENTS: introduced, almost universal

OIL BEETLE
Meloe tuccius Rossi

FAMILY: Meloidae
SIZE: reaches 4 cm.
HABITAT: low and mid-altitudes.
COMMENTS: widely distributed.

TORTOISE BEETLE
Cassida hemisphaerica   Herbst

FAMILY: Chrysomelidae
SIZE: up to 7 mm.
HABITAT: low zone and farmland.
COMMENTS: fedds on leaves of the daisy and mint families.

RED-EDGED LEAF BEETLE
Chrysolina gypsophilae grossepunctata Lindberg

FAMILY: Chrysomelidae
SIZE: up to 1 cm.
HABITAT: low altitudes.
COMMENTS: feeds on plants of the genera *Argyranthemum, Centaurea, Launaea,* etc.

SAGE LEAF BEETLE
Chrysolina gemina   Brullé

FAMILY: Chrysomelidae
SIZE: up to 10 mm.
HABITAT: mid altitudes up to the mountains, feeding on members of the mint family.
COMMENTS: endemic Canarian species.

PEA BEETLE
Bruchus rufimanus Herbst.

FAMILY: Bruchidae
SIZE: up to 5 mm.
HABITAT: common in fields of vegetables specially legumes.
COMMENTS: introduced by man from Europe.

CANARIAN SNOUT BEETLE
Herpysticus eremita Olivier

FAMILY: Curculionidae
SIZE: up to 1.8 cm.
HABITAT: dry areas of the low and middle zones.
COMMENTS: endemic to the Canaries.

BLOSSOM WEEVIL
Laparocerus tessellatus Brullé

FAMILY: Curculionidae
SIZE: up to 8 mm.
HABITAT: laurel forests.
COMMENTS: endemic to the Canaries.

CABBAGE WEVIL
Ceutorrhynchus quadridens   Schön.

FAMILY: Curculionidae
SIZE: only 3 mm.
HABITAT: farmland on *Brassica* species.
COMMENTS: European origin.

GRANARY WEEVIL
Sitophilus granarius   L.

FAMILY: Curculionidae
SIZE: up to 3 mm.
HABITAT: low zone, in houses, warehouses, etc.
COMMENTS: cosmopolitan.

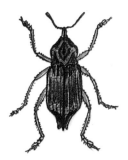

Acalles argillosus   Schön.

FAMILY: Curculionidae
SIZE: up to 1 cm.
HABITAT: dry areas, on the stems of *Senecio kleinia*.
COMMENTS: endemic to the western

PAINTED LADY
Cynthia cardui L.

FAMILY: Nymphalidae
SIZE: wingspan up to 6 cm.
HABITAT: from the lowest zones up to
2000 m.
COMMENTS: the larva feeds on this-
tles (*Silybum, Galactites*).

AMERICAN PAINTED LADY
Cynthia virginensis Drury

FAMILY: Nymphalidae
SIZE: wingspan up to 6 cm.
HABITAT: mountain regions
COMMENTS: the larva feeds on net-
tles and Compositae.

INDIAN RED ADMIRAL
Vanessa vulcania Latreille y Godart

SIZE: wingspan up to 7 cm.
HABITAT: at the margins of the forests
COMMENTS: the larva feeds on net-
tles, especially *Urtica morifolia*.

RED ADMIRAL
Vanessa atalanta L.

FAMILY: Nymphalidae
SIZE: wingspan up to 6 cm.
HABITAT: fields and gardens up to 2000 m.
COMMENTS: the larva feeds on Urticaceae and species of *Carduus*.

CARDINAL
Pandoriana pandora seitzi Fruhstorfer

FAMILY: Nymphalidae
SIZE: wingspan up to 8.5 cm.
HABITAT: preferably woodlands.
COMMENTS: the larva feeds on plants of the genera *Viola & Ruta*.

QUEEN OF SPAIN FRITILLARY
Issoria lathonia   L

FAMILY: Nymphalidae
SIZE: wingspan up to 4.6 cm.
HABITAT: from the coastline to over 2000 m.
COMMENTS: the larva feeds on species of *Viola.*

CANARIAN SPECKLED WOOD
Pararge xiphioides   Staudinger

FAMILY: Satyridae
SIZE: wingspan up to 5.5 cm.
HABITAT: In most habitats from the
coast to the high peaks.
COMMENTS: the larva feeds on gras-
ses.

MEADOW BROWN
Maniola jurtina fortunata   Alphéraky

FAMILY: Satyridae
SIZE: the wingspan is about 5.5 cm.
HABITAT: from sea-level to over
2000m. in fields and woodlands.
COMMENTS: the nocturnal larva
feeds on grasses.

CANARIAN GRAYLING
Hyparchia wysii Christ

FAMILY: Satyridae
SIZE: the wingspan is up to 6.7 cm.
HABITAT: Pine forests and mountain
zones.
COMMENTS: a Canarian endemic
species which has a local subspecies
gomera from the island of La Gomera.
The larva feeds on Graminae (grasses).

AFRICAN MONARCH, plain tiger
Danaus chrysippus L.

FAMILY: Danaidae
SIZE: wingspan up to 7.5 cm.
HABITAT: dry, open areas below 600 m., especially in the Summer.
COMMENTS: the larva feeds on species of the family Asclepiadaceae.

MONARCH, milkweed butterfly
Danaus plexippus L.

FAMILY: Danaidae
SIZE: wingspan up to 10.5 cm.
HABITAT: lower and middle zones, gardens.
COMMENTS: this is the largest Canarian butterfly. The larva feeds on plants of the *Asclepias* family.

CANARY ISLANDS SKIPPER
Thymelicus christi Rebel

FAMILY: Hesperiidae
SIZE: wingspan up to 2.4 cm.
HABITAT: fields, woods etc. from the coast to the highest point of the island.
COMMENTS: A Canarian endemic species, the larva feeds on grasses of the genus *Bromus*. The adult is most frequently seen in Summer.

SMALL COPPER
Lycaena phlaeas   L.

FAMILY: Lycaenidae
SIZE: wingspan about 3.2 cm.
HABITAT: from sea-level to the peaks of the island.
COMMENTS: the larva feeds on plants of the family Polygonaceae.

LONG-TAILED BLUE
Lampides boeticus   L.

FAMILY: Lycaenidae
SIZE: wingspan up to 5 cm.
HABITAT: from the mid-zones to the highest mountains.
COMMENTS: the larva feeds on Leguminosae, living in the seed-pods. An almost world-wide warm-temperate and tropical species.

CANARY ISLANDS BLUE
Cyclyrius webbianus   Brullé

FAMILY: Lycaenidae
SIZE: wingspan up to 3 cm.
HABITAT: abundant in pine forest areas, rarer in other woodlands.
COMMENTS: the caterpillar feeds mainly on Leguminosae, *Teline, Lotus, Adenocarpus* etc.

155

AFRICAN BLUE
Zizeeria knysna　　Trimen

FAMILY: Lycaenidae
SIZE: wingspan up to 2.5 cm.
HABITAT: frquent in the lower zone.
COMMENTS: a mainly African spe-
cies which extends to Southern Spain,
the larva feeds on Leguminosae.

LARGE WHITE
Pieris cheiranthi　　Hubner

FAMILY: Pieridae
SIZE: wingspan up to 7 cm.
HABITAT: from sea-level to the moun-
tains, rather irregularly distributed.
COMMENTS:　　Canary　endemic,
represented on La Gomera by subsp.
Cheiranthi. The caterpillar feeds on
Tropaeolum majus or on species of the
family Cruciferae.

SMALL WHITE
Pieris rapae　　L.

FAMILY: Pieridae
SIZE: wingspan up to 5 cm.
HABITAT: very common, from the coast
to the mountains in almost all vegetation
types, especially in cultivated areas.
COMMENTS:　　the　larva　feeds　on
Tropaeolum majus and on Cruciferae
and Resedaceae.

BATH WHITE
Pontia daplidice   L.

FAMILY: Pieridae
SIZE: wingspan up to 5 cm.
HABITAT: common from the coast to the mountain peaks in practically all vegetation types.
COMMENTS: the larva feeds on Cruciferae and Resedaceae.

CLOUDED YELLOW
Colias crocea   Fourcroy

FAMILY Pieridae
SIZE: wingspan about 5 cm.
HABITAT: open habitats and in forests from sea-level to the mountains.
COMMENTS: the larva feeds on plants of the family Leguminosae.

CLEOPATRA
Gonepteryx cleobule   Hubner

FAMILY: Pieridae
SIZE: wingspan up to 6.5 cm.
HABITAT: usually in the laurel forests and tree-heath woodland from about 600-1800m.
COMMENTS: a Canary Islands endemic. The subsp. *cleobule* is present on La Gomera. The larva feeds on the laurel forest tree *Rhamnus glandulosa.*

DEATH'S HEAD HAWK MOTH
Acherontia atropos   L.

FAMILY: Sphingidae
SIZE: wingspan up to 10 cm.
HABITAT: mainly in the lower zone, from sea-level to the edges of the forests.
COMMENTS: easily recognised by the skull-like marking on the dorsal side of the thorax. Nocturnal and very abundant in Spring and Summer. The larva feeds on Solanaceae and Bignoniaceae.

CONVOLVULUS HAWK MOTH
Agrius convolvuli batatae   Christ

FAMILY: Sphingidae
SIZE: wingspan up to 10 cm.
HABITAT: from sea-level to the middle zone.
COMMENTS: nocturnal, abundant in Spring and Summer, the larva feeds mainly on members of the family Convolvulaceae and on grape vines.

SPURGE HAWK MOTH
Hyles euphorbiae tithymali   Boisduval

FAMILY: Sphingidae
SIZE: wingspan up to 7cm.
HABITAT: from sea-level to the mountain zones.
COMMENTS: nocturnal, the caterpillar feeds on shrubby spurges (*Euphorbia broussonetii, E. berthelotii.*).

HOUSE FLY
Musca domestica   L.

FAMILY: Muscidae
SIZE: up to 8 mm.
HABITAT: houses, gardens, etc. Close
to decomposition.
COMMENTS: cosmopolitan, present
on all the islands.

STABLE FLY
Stomoxys calcitrans   L.

FAMILY: Muscidae
SIZE: up to 7.5 mm.
HABITAT: around farms.
COMMENTS: adults feed on mammal,
even human, blood and spread disease
between animals.

HOVER FLY
Sphaerophoria scripta   L.

FAMILY: Syrphidae
SIZE: up to 12 mm.
HABITAT: lives on flowers of the daisy
family.
COMMENTS: a Macronesian species,
found in the Canaries, Madeira and
The Azores.

EUROPEAN HOVER FLY
Scaeva pyrastri L.

FAMILY: Syrphidae
SIZE: up to 15 mm.
HABITAT: adults usually on flowerheads
of the daisy family.
COMMENTS: larvae feed on aphids.

DRONE FLY
Chrysotoxum triarcuatum Macquart.

FAMILY: Syrphidae
SIZE: up to 1.5 cm.
HABITAT: amongst dense vegetation.
COMMENTS: the larva feed on rotting
wood, the adults on nectar.

MOSQUITO
Culex pipiens L.

FAMILY: Culicidae
SIZE: up to 5 mm.
HABITAT: around stagnant water.
COMMENTS: females feed on the
blood of mammals, the males on nectar.

DIPTERA (CONT.)

DRONE FLY
Eristalis tenax   L.

FAMILY: Syrphidae
SIZE: up to 15 mm.
HABITAT: the larva, rat-tailed mag-
gots, have a long breathing tube and live
in stagnant water.
COMMENTS: cosmopolitan and found
on all the islands. Often confused with
the honey bee.

HORSE FLY
Hippobosca equina L.

FAMILY: Hipposboscidae.
SIZE: up to 8 mm.
HABITAT: in areas of dense vegetation.
COMMENTS: feeds on the blood of
domestic animals.

HYMENOPTERA

DIGGER WASP
Bembix flavescens flavescens Smith

FAMILY: Sphecidae
SIZE: 2.8 cm.
HABITAT: dry areas of the island.
Coast line and beaches
COMMENTS: female excavates a
sandy burrow and feeds the grubs on
the larva of Diptera.

SAND WASP
Podalonia tydei   Le Guillou

FAMILY: Sphecidae
SIZE: up to 2.5 cm.
HABITAT: found close to sandy areas.
COMMENTS: present on all seven islands.

BANDED DIGGER WASP
Cerceris concinna   Brullé

FAMILY: Sphecidae
SIZE: up to 13 mm.
HABITAT: low altitudes.
COMMENTS: female digs a burrow in the sand and hunts Hemiptera larva.

WHITE-TAILED BUMBLE BEE
Bombus canariensis   Pérez

FAMILY: Apidae.
SIZE: up to 2 cm.
HABITAT: areas where flowers of Labiatae and Leguminosae are abundant.
COMMENTS: makes a nest in the ground and the populations are not usually numerous. It is a social insect.

ICHNEUMONID FLY
Ophion obscuratus   Fabricius

FAMILY: Ichneumonidae
SIZE: up to 2 cm.
HABITAT: areas of dense vegetation.
Garden, etc.
COMMENTS: larva feed on moth and
butterfly larva.

HONEY BEE
Apis mellifera   L.

FAMILY: Apidae
SIZE: up to 17 mm.
HABITAT: wild colonies live in trees.
COMMENTS: a social species introdu-
ced by man.

SOLITARY BEE
Anthophora alluaudi   Pérez

FAMILY: Anthophoridae
SIZE: up to 14 mm.
HABITAT: feeds from tubular flowers
such as those of *Echium.*
COMMENTS: nests in the ground and
mud walls. An important pollinator.

RUBY-TAILED WASP
Chrysis magnidens   Pérez

FAMILY: Chrysididae
SIZE: up to 1 cm.
HABITAT: sunny places.
COMMENTS: the females put their eggs in the nests of other wasp. The larva feed on the stored food as well as on the eggs and larva found there.

SOLITARY FLOWER BEE
Anthidium canariense Mavromoustakis

FAMILY: Megachilidae
SIZE: up to 8 mm.
HABITAT: low and mid altitudes.
COMMENTS: endemic to La Gomera and Gran Canaria.

PAPER WASP
Polistes gallicus   L.

FAMILY: Vespidae
SIZE: up to 16 mm.
HABITAT: low zone of the island.
COMMENTS: the nest is built almost anywhere; roofs, trees, wood, windows, etc.

GERMAN WASP
Paravespula germanica Fabricius

FAMILY: Vespidae
SIZE: up to 2 cm.
HABITAT: low and mid zones.
COMMENTS: present omly on the central and western islands.

ARGENTINE ANT
Iridomyrmex humilis Mayr

FAMILY: Formicidae
SIZE: up to 3.5 mm.
HABITAT: colonies are common in banana plantations where the ant obtains honeydew from cochinneal.
COMMENTS: introduced, probably with sugar cane.

BLACK ANT
Camponotus atlantis Emery

FAMILY: Formicidae
SIZE: up to 12.5 mm.
HABITAT: North coast and mid altitudes.
COMMENTS: present on all the islands.

FISH

Most of the marine fish found in the Canary Islands waters are typical of the warmer regions of the eastern atlantic Ocean which extend from the South of the british isles to the mediterranean sea and the coastal waters of Western Africa. Most of the species illustrated in this guide can be seen close to the coast whilst snorkeling or in the fishing harbours and markets of the island.

Fish form an important element of the rich but fragile coastal ecosystem of the Canaries. Their habitats can easily be damaged or destroyed by over-development, lack of planning in coastal tourism, overfishing and uncontrolled pollution.

The principal habitats of fish are over rocks or in seagrass meadows on sandy bottoms between the littoral zone to the border of the island platform where this plunges to a depth of about 800 m.

There is enormous confusion over local common names of some fish species and these vary considerably from island to island and even between different local fishing communities on the same island.

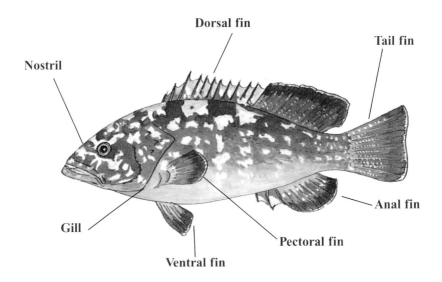

General view of a bony fish

FISH (CHONDRICHTHYES)

TRIAKIDAE

SMOOTH HOUND
Mustelus mustelus   L.

SIZE: up to 160 cm.
HABITAT: benthic. On sandy or muddy bottoms between 2 and 350 m.
COMMENTS: eats molluscs and crustaceans.

SOUALIDAE

PIKED DOGFISH
Raja clavata L.

SIZE: up to 120 cm.
HABITAT: benthic. On sandy and muddy substrates between 100 and 900 m.
COMMENTS: a fish eater.

CARCHARHINIDAE

BLUE SHARK
Prionace glauca   L.

SIZE: up to 400 cm.
HABITAT: littoral epipelagic and oceanic.
COMMENTS: feeds on fish such as mackerel and sardines.

FISH

SPHYRNIDAE

HAMMERHEAD SHARK
Mustelus mustelus   L.

SIZE: up to 400 cm.
HABITAT: littoral epipelagic and open water close to land.
COMMENTS: feeds on fish and invertebrates, hunting close to the shore.

RAJIDAE

THORNBACK RAY
Raja clavata   L.

SIZE: up to 130 cm.
HABITAT: benthic. Sand and rock bottoms between 20 and 180 m.
COMMENTS:feeds on fish, small molluscs and other invertebrates.

DASYATIDAE

COMMON STING RAY
Dasyatis pastinaca   L.

SIZE: up to 60 cm. wide.
HABITAT: benthic. On sandy and partially rocky bottoms between 5 and 200 m.
COMMENTS: feeds on small fish and invertebrates.

RAINBOW WRASSE
Coris julis L.

SIZE: up to 25 cm.
HABITAT: benthic. Rocky and sand/rock bottoms between 2 and 190 m.
COMMENTS: common.

PEACOCK WRASSE
Thalassoma pavo L.

SIZE: up to 22 cm.
HABITAT: benthic, to depths of 200 m. Common on all weedy bottoms.
COMMENTS: used as livebait for abae (*Mycteroperca fusca*) fishing.

CLEAVER WRASSE
Xyrichthys novacula L.

SIZE: reaches 30 cm.
HABITAT: benthic, found down to 50 m on sandy bottoms and in meadows of seagrass (*Cymodocea nodosa*).
COMMENTS: when disturbed it burrows rapidly into the sand.

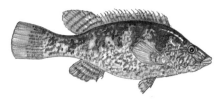

BALLAN WRASSE
Labrus bergylta Ascanius

SIZE: up to 55cm.
HABITAT: benthic. On bottoms with heavy weed cover between 4 and 50 m.
COMMENTS: common around the eastern islands, occasional around the western islands.

GREY WRASSE
Centrolabrus trutta Lowe

SIZE: up to 20 cm.
HABITAT: benthic. Found on rocky bottoms with dense weed cover down to 20 m.
COMMENTS: common.

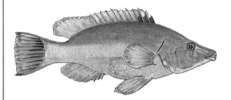

HOGFISH
Pseudolepidaplois scrofa Valenciennes

SIZE: reaches 65 cm.
HABITAT: benthic. On rocky and mixed bottoms between 5 and 150 m.
COMMENTS: common but listed as threatened on the red list of endangered species. Sexually dimorphic.

SERRANIDAE

WRECKFISH
Polyprion americanus Schneider

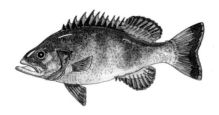

SIZE: reaches 180 cm.
HABITAT: benthic, on rocky bottoms between 200 and 800 m.
COMMENTS: epipelagic, juveniles often found at the surface.

DUSKY GROUPER
Epinephelus marginatus Lowe

SIZE: up to 160 cm.
HABITAT: benthic, down to 200 m. Hides in or near caves during the day.
COMMENTS: the juveniles (pups) are often found in inter-tidal pools. Listed as threatened on the red list of endangered species.

COMB GROUPER
Mycteroperca fusca Lowe

SIZE: up to 90 cm.
HABITAT: benthic, on rocky bottoms down to 150 m.
COMMENTS: occasionally seen hunting in open water close to the coast.

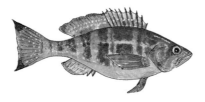

BLACKTAIL COMBER
Serranus atricauda   Günther

SIZE: up to 45 cm.
HABITAT: benthic, on rocky bottoms
between 3 and 150 m.
COMMENTS: common. Excellent
eating.

COMMON COMBER
Serranus cabrilla   L.

SIZE: up to 45 cm.
HABITAT: benthic, between 5 and
300m. on rocky bottoms.
COMMENTS: common. Along with
the previous species this is one of the
most sought after species of coastal fis-
heries.

SWALLOW-TAIL SEA PERCH
Anthias anthias   L.

SIZE: up to 25 cm.
HABITAT: benthic, on rocky bottoms
and in caves between 30 and 300 m.
COMMENTS: common, often forming
small shoals.

POMACENTRIDAE

BLACK DAMSEL FISH
Abudefduf luridus   Cuvier

SIZE: only 14 cm.
HABITAT: on rocky bottoms down to
60 m. Benthic.
COMMENTS: common, feeding on
algae and small crustaceans.

BAND-TAIL CHROMIS
Chromis limbatus   Valenciennes

SIZE: reaches 15 cm.
HABITAT: benthic to epibenthic, (2 to
100 m.). Often seen in shoals over rocky
bottoms.
COMMENTS: common.

BERYCIDAE

COMMON BERYX
Beryx decadactylus   Cuvier

SIZE: up to 55 cm.
HABITAT: rocky bottoms between 400
and 700 m.
COMMENTS: common, often forming
small shoals.

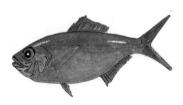

FISH

BERYCIDAE

SLENDER BERYX
Beryx splendens   Lowe

SIZE: up to 45 cm.
HABITAT: rocky bottoms between 400 and 700 m.
COMMENTS: common, forming small shoals.

PRIACANTIDAE

GLASSEYE
Heteropriacanthus cruentatus Lacepede

SIZE: up to 30cm.
HABITAT: benthic. In caves and around rocks between 5 and 30 m.
COMMENTS: common, nocturnal. Feeds on small crustaceans.

APOGONIDAE

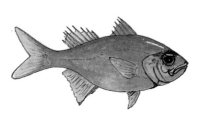

CARDINAL FISH
Apogon imberbis L.

SIZE: only 10 cm.
HABITAT: benthic (3 to 50 m.). In rocky caves.
COMMENTS: common. The male incubates the eggs in his mouth.

HAEMULIDAE

BASTARD GRUNT
Pomadasys incisus   Bowdich

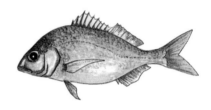

SIZE: up to 40 cm.
HABITAT: benthic, on rock and mixed bottoms from 3 to 100 m.
COMMENTS: common, feeding on small invertebrates.

STRIPED GRUNT
Parapristipoma octolineatum   Valenciennes

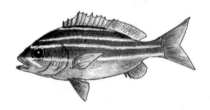

SIZE: up to 50 cm.
HABITAT: benthic. Common on rocky bottoms and in caves. 20 to 150 m.
COMMENTS: forms small shoals. Feeds on invertebrates. Very good eating.

LUTJANIDAE

CANARY DRUM
Umbrina canariensis   Valenciennes

SIZE: up to 63 cm.
HABITAT: benthic. On sand/rock and rock bottoms between 5 and 150 m.
COMMENTS: a solitary species, which occasionally forms small shoals. Feeds on molluscs and crustaceans. The juvenile is referred to locally as Maria Francisca.

SKIPJACK TUNA
Katsuwonus pelamis L.

SIZE: up to 130 cm. (17 kg.)
HABITAT: oceanic, epipelagic. Sometimes seen close to the coast.
COMMENTS: in Canary waters from Spring to Autumn, being most common during Summer.

ALBACORE
Thunnus alalunga Bonnaterre

SIZE: up to 125 cm. (25 kg.)
HABITAT: oceanic, pelagic.
COMMENTS: common around the islands between November and April. Feeds on other fish, squid and large crustaceans.

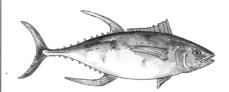

YELLOWFIN TUNNY
Thunnus albacares Bonnaterre

SIZE: up to 220 cm. (30 kg.)
HABITAT: oceanic, epipelagic.
COMMENTS: in Canary waters from July through October.

SCOMBRIDAE (cont.)

BIG-EYE TUNNY
Thunnus obesus Lowe

SIZE: up to 250 cm.
HABITAT: oceanic/pelagic.
COMMENTS: common between
February and April.

BLUEFIN TUNNY
Thunnus thynnus thynnus L.

SIZE: up to 310 m. and 250 kg.
HABITAT: oceanic, pelagic.
COMMENTS: common from February
through April.

FRIGATE TUNA
Auxis rochei Risso

SIZE: up to 60 cm.
HABITAT: littoral, epipelagic.
Sometimes appears near the coast.
COMMENTS: most common during
the Winter months.

SCOMBRIDAE (cont.)

CHUB MACKEREL
Scomber japonicus   Houttuyn

SIZE: up to 52 cm.
HABITAT: littoral, pelagic. Found to depths of 250 m.
COMMENTS: most common during the Summer and Autumn.

ISTIOPHORIDAE

BLUE MARLIN
Makaira nigricans   Lacepède

SIZE: grows to 450 cm. and 650 kg.
HABITAT: oceanic, epipelagic.
COMMENTS: common in Canary waters during the Spring and Autumn.

XIPHIIDAE

SWORDFISH
Xiphias gladius   L.

SIZE: grows to 480 cm. and 650 kg.
HABITAT: epipelagic and mesopelagic. Spends the day at depths from 200 to 500 m., surfacing at night.
COMMENTS: common throughout the year.

CARANGIDAE

BLUE JACK MACKEREL
Trachurus picturatus   T.E. Bowdich

SIZE: up to 50 cm.
HABITAT: littoral pelagic, from the surface down to 250 m.
COMMENTS: rarely grow longer than 20 cm. in Canary waters.

GUELLY JACK
Pseudocaranx dentex   Bloch & Schneider

SIZE: up to 90 cm. and 8 kg.
HABITAT: epibenthic to pelagic. From the coastline down to 100 m.
COMMENTS: moves up to the surface at night to feed on small fish and invertebrates.

DERBIO
Trachinotus ovatus   L.

SIZE: up to 45 cm.
HABITAT: littoral pelagic, often close to the coast.
COMMENTS: often seen in small shoals throughout the Summer and Autumn.

CLUPEIDAE

PILCHARD
Sardina pilchardus   Walbaum

SIZE: up to 22 cm.
HABITAT: littoral pelagic. Often close to the coast but occasionally as deep as 250 m.
COMMENTS: two other species of sardine appear in Canary waters; *Sardinella aurita* and *Sardinella maderensis*.

MUGILIDAE

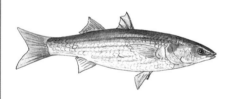

GOLDEN MULLET
Liza aurata   Risso

SIZE: up to 50 cm.
HABITAT: coastal waters, no deeper than 20 m.
COMMENTS: lives in small shoals.

THICK-LIPPED GREY MULLET
Chelon labrosus   Risso

SIZE: up to 50 cm.
HABITAT: near the coast, preferably in less than 20 . of water.
COMMENTS: feeds on algae and debris.

PANDORA
Pagellus erythrinus L.

SIZE: up to 65 cm.
HABITAT: mixed sand and rock bottoms between 100 and 200 m.
COMMENTS: feeds on molluscs and crustaceans. More common around Gran Canaria and the Eastern islands.

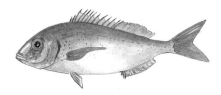

COMMON SEA BREAM
Pagrus pagrus L.

SIZE: reaches lengths of 75 cm.
HABITAT: between 10 and 250 m. on sandy and rocky bottoms.
COMMENTS: feds on molluscs and crustaceans. Present around all the islands where the juveniles are called " Palletas ".

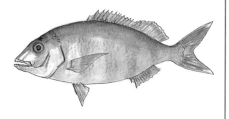

RED-BANDED SEA BREAM
Pagrus auriga Valenciennes

SIZE: up to 90 cm.
HABITAT: benthic (5 to 250 cm.). Rocky and sand bottoms.
COMMENTS: present around all the islands where the juveniles are called "Catalineta". Feeds on molluscs and crustaceans.

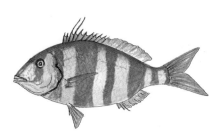

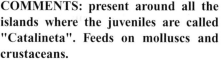

SPARIDAE (CONT.)

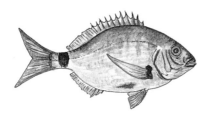

ANNULAR SEA BREAM
Diplodus annularis   L.

SIZE: up to 25 cm.
HABITAT: benthic. Down to 25 m.
COMMENTS: forms small shoals.
Feeds on algae and small invertebrates.

SHARPSNOUT SEA BREAM
Diplodus puntazzo   Cetti

SIZE: up to 60 cm.
HABITAT: benthic. Down to 250 m.
COMMENTS: feeds on plant matter
and debris.

2-BANDED SEA BREAM
Diplodus vulgaris   St. Hilaire

SIZE: up to 45 cm.
HABITAT: between 10 and 100 m. on
all bottoms.
COMMENTS: present around all the
islands.

SPARIDAE (CONT.)

WHITE SEA BREAM
Diplodus sargus cadenati   de la Paz ,
Bauchot y Daget.

SIZE: up to 45 cm.
HABITAT: rock and mixed sand/rock
bottoms down to 250 m.
COMMENTS: forms small shoals.
Present around all the islands.

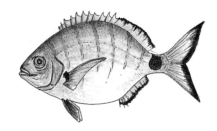

ZEBRA SEA BREAM
Diplodus cervinus cervinus   Lowe

SIZE: up to 55 cm.
HABITAT: rock and mixed sand/rock
bottoms down to 100 m.
COMMENTS: found in small shoals
around all the islands.

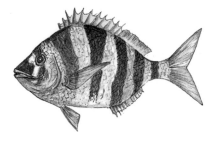

SADDLED BREAM
Oblada melanura   L.

SIZE: up to 35 cm.
HABITAT: over rocks and sand in less
than 30 m. of water.
COMMENTS: eats algae and crustaceans.

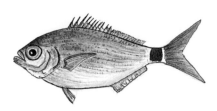

SPARIDAE (CONT.)

PINK DENTEX.
Dentex (Cheimerius) gibbosus Rafinesque

SIZE: up to 1 m. and 20 kg.
HABITAT: mainly on rock and rock/sand bottoms between 10 and 200 m.
COMMENTS: the juveniles ("Serrudas") come closer to the coast than the adults.

COMMON DENTEX
Dentex dentex L.

SIZE: grows to 100 cm.
HABITAT: benthic, on rocky bottoms from 10 to 200m.
COMMENTS: more frequent around the Eastern islands.

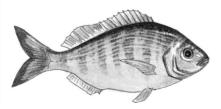

BERMUDA CHUB
Kyphosus sectator L.

SIZE: up to 80 cm.
HABITAT: littoral. Over rocky and mixed bottoms down to 50 m.
COMMENTS: tends to form small shoals. Due to the strong flavour of algae its flesh is not appreciated in the Canaries.

SPARIDAE (CONT.)

SALEMA
Sarpa salpa L.

SIZE: up to 30 cm.
HABITAT: rocky and mixed sand and rock bottoms down to 50 m.
COMMENTS: forms large shoals. Salema flesh tastes strongly of algae and is not often eaten in the Islands.

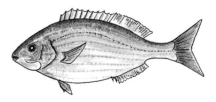

BOGUE
Boops boops L.

SIZE: reaches 35 cm.
HABITAT: epibenthic to pelagic over all bottoms. Found down to 250 m.
COMMENTS: common but not eaten in some areas where it lives in polluted water and near sewage outflows.

MACRORAMPHOSIDAE

SNIPE FISH
Macroramphosus scolopax L.

SIZE: up to 20 cm.
HABITAT: the juveniles are pelagic, living in oceanic waters. Adults are found on rocky bottoms down to 200 m.
COMMENTS: during the Spring the juveniles sometimes throw themselves on to the shore, probably to escape predators.

TETRAODONTIDAE

SHARPNOSE PUFFERFISH
Canthigaster rostrata Bloch

SIZE: only 10 cm.
HABITAT: benthic. Around rocks and mixed rock and sand bottoms in less than 30 m. of water.
COMMENTS: can inflate itself when threatened.

PUFFER FISH
Sphoeroides spengleri   Bloch

SIZE: up to 25 cm.
HABITAT: benthic. On rock and rock/sand bottoms down to 60 m.
COMMENTS: can inflate itself considerably when in danger.

DIODONTIDAE

SPINY PUFFERFISH
Chilomycterus atringa   L.

SIZE: up to 45 cm.
HABITAT: benthic. In caves and crevices of rocky bottoms down to 50 m.
COMMENTS: occasional around La Gomera but common around El Hierro.

SYNODONTIDAE

LIZARD FISH
Synodus saurus L.

SIZE: up to 42 cm.
HABITAT: benthic. On rocky and mixed sand and rock bottoms down to 100 m.
COMMENTS: feeds on small fish and crustaceans.

TRACHINIDAE

GREATER WEEVER
Trachinus draco L.

SIZE: up to 35 cm.
HABITAT: benthic. On sandy, littoral bottoms down to 50 m.
COMMENTS: found buried in the sand. Its poisonous dorsal spines can deliver a very painful sting.

SCORPAENIDAE

ROSEFISH
Helicolenus dactylopterus dactylopterus
Delaroche

SIZE: up to 45 cm.
HABITAT: benthic. On rock and weed covered rock bottoms between 300 and 1.000 m.
COMMENTS: common. A good eating fish.

ORANGE SCORPION FISH
Pontinus kuhlii   Bowdich

SIZE: up to 50 cm.
HABITAT: benthic. On rocky bottoms and amongst weed between 150 and 400 m.
COMMENTS: common and very good eating.

SCORPION FISH
Scorpaena scrofa   L.

SIZE: between 15 and 50 cm.
HABITAT: benthic. On rocky and sand/rock bottoms down to 200 m.
COMMENTS: good eating but can give dangerous stings with some of its spines.

SMALL-SCALED SCORPION FISH
Scorpaena porcus   L.

SIZE: up to 25 cm.
HABITAT: benthic. Rock and mixed sand and rock bottoms down to 200 m.
COMMENTS: changes colour to match its surroundings. Good eating.

BALISTIDAE

GREY TRIGGER FISH
Balistes carolinensis   Gmelin

SIZE: up to 60 cm.
HABITAT: epibenthic to benthic. On mixed sand and rock bottoms down to 100 m.
COMMENTS: common around the western islands. Excellent eating.

MONACANTHIDAE

YELLOW TRIGGER FISH
Stephanolepis hispidus   L.

SIZE: up to 26 cm.
HABITAT: epibenthic to benthic. Mixed sand/rock bottoms down to 180 m.
COMMENTS: very common around the eastern islands. Good eating once skinned.

ZEIDAE

JOHN DORY
Zeus faber   L.

SIZE: up to 90 cm.
HABITAT: epibenthic to benthic. On all bottoms down to 200 m.
COMMENTS: known as Saint Peter's Fish, the black spots being marks his fingers left when he caught one. Very good eating.

FISH

BELONIDAE

GREENBONE GARFISH
Belone belone gracilis   Lowe

SIZE: up to 90 cm. long.
HABITAT: littoral epipelagic.
COMMENTS: appears in small shoals close to the coast during the Summer. Good eating.

SCORPAENIDAE

SAURY PIKE
Scomberesox saurus saurus   Walbaum

SIZE: up to 60 cm.
HABITAT: oceanic, epipelagic and littoral.
COMMENTS: lives in large shoals.

SPHYRAENIDAE

BARRACUDA
Sphyraena viridensis   Cuvier

SIZE: up to 160 m.
HABITAT: littoral waters, especially by steep coasts and cliffs.
COMMENTS: common, forming large shoals while spawning.

MURENIDAE

SHARK-TOOTH MORAY EEL
Gymnothorax **spp.**

SIZE: reaches 100 cm.
HABITAT: rocky bottoms from the sho-
reline down to 300 m.
COMMENTS: common around the
Western islands. Good eating.

MORAY EEL
Muraena helena **L.**

SIZE: up to 135 cm.
HABITAT: caves and rocky crevices
down to 800 m.
COMMENTS: feeds on small fish,
crustaceans and carrion.

CONGRIDAE

CONGER EEL
Conger conger **Artedi (L.)**

SIZE: up to 200 m.
HABITAT: benthic. On rocky bottoms
down to 800 m.
COMMENTS: comes out at night to
feed on fish, crustaceans and cephalopods.

FISH

CORYPHAENIDAE

DOLPHIN FISH
Coryphaena hippurus   L.

SIZE: up to 200 cm.
HABITAT: oceanic epipelagic.
Sometimes comes in close to the coast.
COMMENTS: common during the
Summer and Autumn. Feeds on small
fish and is often caught by tunny fis-
hermen.

GOBIDAE

ROCK GOBY
Gobius paganellus   L.

SIZE: only 10 cm.
HABITAT: benthic. Inter-tidal pools,
rock and pebble bottoms of the infralittoral zone. Found in less than 10 m. of
water.
COMMENTS: common around all the
islands. Feeds on small invertebrates.

MADEIRAN GOBY
Mauligobius maderensis   Valenciennes

SIZE: up to 10 cm.
HABITAT: benthic. In inter-tidal pools.
COMMENTS: feeds on small inverte-
brates. Common around all the islands.

BLENIIDAE

BLENNY
Lipophrys trigloides   Valenciennes

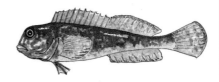

SIZE: up to 11 cm.
HABITAT: benthic. In inter-tidal pools.
COMMENTS: common to all the islands.

MONTAGU'S BLENNY
Coryphoblennius galerita   L.

SIZE: up to 12 cm.
HABITAT: benthic. Found in inter-tidal pools.
COMMENTS: feeds on small invertebrates.

ATLANTIC BLENNY, RUBBER EYE
Ophioblennius atlanticus atlanticus Valenc.

SIZE: up to 20 cm.
HABITAT: benthic. On rocky bottoms down to 15 m. Harbour walls etc.
COMMENTS: juveniles often found in inter-tidal pools.

MULLIDAE

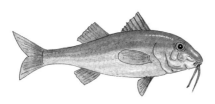

RED MULLET
Mullus surmuletus   L.

SIZE: up to 40 cm.
HABITAT: benthic. Sandy or weedy bottoms close to beds of *Cymodocea nodosa* (sea grass).
COMMENTS: more common around the central and eastern islands.

TRIGLIDAE

RED GURNARD
Chelidonichthys lastoviza   Brünnich

SIZE: up to 40 cm.
HABITAT: benthic. Sandy and rock/sand bottoms between 10 and 150 m.
COMMENTS: more common around the eastern islands.

ATHERINIDAE

SAND SMELT
Atherina (Hepsetia) presbyter   Cuvier

SIZE: up to 14 cm.
HABITAT: littoral pelagic, often close to the shore.
COMMENTS: common but included in the red lists of endangered species.

FISH

GADIDAE

FORKBEARD
Phycis phycis　　L.

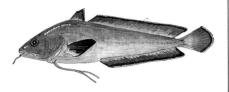

SIZE: up to 65 cm.
HABITAT: benthic. Rock caves and
cavities down to 350 m.
COMMENTS: common around the
islands. Excellent eating.

SCARIDAE

PARROT FISH
Sparisoma (Euscarus) cretense　　L.

SIZE: up to 70 cm.
HABITAT: benthic, down to 100 m. On
rocky and mixed bottoms with dense
algal growth.
COMMENTS: sexually dimorphic, the
female being brightly coloured and the
male greyish brown. Often found in
shoals.

BOTHIDAE

FLOUNDER
Bothus podas maderensis　　Delaroche

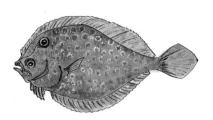

SIZE: up to 25 cm.
HABITAT: benthic. On sandy of
rock/sand bottoms down to 90 m.
COMMENTS: a subspecies only known
from the Canaries and Madeira.

The amphibians are represented in the Canary islands by two species of frogs, *Rana perezii*, the common frog and *Hyla meridionalis*, the green tree frog.

After the birds, the reptiles are the biggest group of terrestrial vertebrates present in the Canaries. They are represented by skinks, geckoes and lizards. There is considerable variation between the islands with numerous different specie and subspecies of each group and an endemic lizard genus Gallotia.

On the island of La Gomera both the frogs are present and the local reptiles are the Gomeran gecko (*Tarantola gomerensis*), the golden skink (*Chalcides viridanus*) which is also found on Tenerife, La Palma and El Hierro, and a local subspecies of the Tenerife lizard (*Gallotia galloti gomerae*).

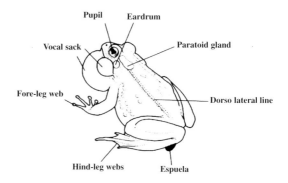

Hints for identifying anphibians

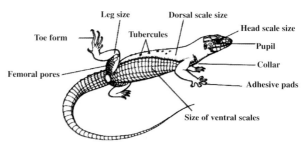

Hints for identifying reptiles

GREEN TREE FROG
Hyla meridionalis. Boettger

SIZE: up to 5.5 cm.
HABITAT: humid areas, gardens, banana plantations, etc.
COMMENTS: introduced from the Southeastern Mediterranean. In the Canaries it tends to croak between seven in the evening and midnight while the temperature is between 12 and 24ºC.

COMMON FROG
Rana perezii. Seoane

SIZE: up to 10 cm.
HABITAT: reservoirs, water tanks, etc. From sea level up to the mountains.
COMMENTS: introduced by man. During the breeding season the males croak day and night, whether they are in or out of the water.

TENERIFE LIZARD
Gallotia galloti gomerae. Boettger & Müller

SIZE: up to 40 cm.
HABITAT: from the coastline up to the mountains.
COMMENTS: Males have blue patchs on their throat and flanks. The Gomeran lizards are a unique subspecies.

GOMERAN GECKO
Tarentola gomerensis. Joger & Bischoff

SIZE: up to 9 cm.
HABITAT: under rocks and amongst stones in dry arid areas. Found all over the island at all altitudes.
COMMENTS: dark colourd and nocturnal. Described as a separate species exclusive to La Gomera in 1985.

GOLDEN SKINK
Chalcides viridanus. Gravenhorst

SIZE: up to 9 cm.
HABITAT: sea level up to 600 m. or so. Found amongst stones and in walls as well as in vegetation.
COMMENTS: endemic to La Gomera, Tenerife and El Hierro.

LEATHERY TURTLE
Dermochelys coriacea. L.

SIZE: up to 190 cm. and 600 kg.
HABITAT: the most coastal species, living in surface waters. Can dive to 200 or even 500 m. to feed.
COMMENTS: this, the largest living turtle, is an occasional visitor to Canary waters. Feeds mainly on jellyfish and tunicates.

HAWKSBILL TURTLE
Eretmochelys imbricata. L.

SIZE: up to 92 cm and 75 cm.
HABITAT: shallow waters around rocky coasts.
COMMENTS: feeds on algae and marine invertebrates such as sponges, sea urchins, molluscs, tunicates, etc.

LOGGERHEAD TURTLE
Caretta caretta L.

SIZE: up to 122 cm.
HABITAT: pelagic. At home in deep ocean and, shallow coastal waters.
COMMENTS: the commonest species. Eats small fish, jellyfish (*Physalia, Velella*) and marine invertebrates such as crustaceans, molluscs, etc.

The avifauna of the Canary islands is relatively rich and occupies a wide variety of habitats from the coast through the forest regions to the highest mountains.

About 65% of the birds are endemic at the species or subspecies level. The endemic species are Fringilla teydea (blue chaffinch), Columba bollii (Bolle's laurel pigeon), Columba junoniae (white-tailed laurel pigeon), Saxicola dacotiae (Fuerteventuran chat) and Haematopus moquini (black oystercatcher).

On the island of La Gomera many of the Canarian endemic birds can be seen though all are shared with at least one of the other islands. The large populations of Bolle's laurel pigeon which nests and lives in the laurel forests and of the white-tailed laurel pigeon which extends beyond the forest margins into the cultivated zones below, are both notable species to look for.

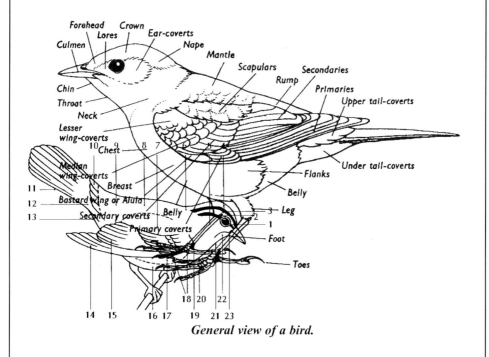

General view of a bird.

PALLID SWIFT
Apus pallidus brehmorum   Hart.

FAMILIY: Apodidae.
SIZE: up to 17 cm.
DESCRIPTION: distinguished from the plain
swift by its greyish colour and white throat.
HABITAT: usually in the lower zone, it
nests in old buildings, cliffs and crevices.
COMMENTS: found on all the islands
especially the central and eastern ones. It
is a Spring and Summer visitor with a
small population.

PLAIN SWIFT
Apus unicolor unicolor   (Jard.)

FAMILY: Apodidae.
SIZE: up to 15 cm.
DESCRIPTION: a gregarious bird, greyish
black in colour with a pale grey throat.
HABITAT: in the lower and middle zones.
Nests on high cliffs between April and July.
COMMENTS: abundant, visits the
Canaries in Spring and Summer and is
absent in the Winter.

ATLANTIC HERRING GULL
Larus argentatus atlantis   Dwight.

FAMILY: Laridae.
SIZE: about 56 cm.
DESCRIPTION: white with the back and
upper wings grey. Legs yellow.
HABITAT: the littoral zone of the island
where it is locally common
COMMENTS: nests in Spring on inaccessible cliffs, feeds on fish and scavenges on
rubbish.

BUZZARD
Buteo buteo insularum Floer

FAMILY: Accipitridae.
SIZE: up to 56 cm.
DESCRIPTION: brown with the lower parts striped with cream or white, especially on the breast.
HABITAT: up to 1000 m. altitude, both in open and forest habitats.
COMMENTS: feeds on small rodents, reptiles and insects.

SPARROWHAWK
Accipiter nisus granti Sharpe

FAMILY: Accipitridae.
SIZE: up to 37 cm.
DESCRIPTION: in flight it differs from the kestrel by its short, rounded wings.
HABITAT: forest zones.
COMMENTS: it usually feeds on small birds.

KESTREL
Falco tinnunculus canariensis Koen.

FAMILY: Falconidae.
SIZE: about 35 cm.
DESCRIPTION: dorsal reddish-chestnut with black markings, lower parts creamish with darker marks, head greyish.
HABITAT: usually open habitats from the coast to the mountains.
COMMENTS: feeds on insects, small rodents and reptiles.

BARBARY PARTRIDGE
Alectoris barbara köenigi   (Reich.)

FAMILY: Phasianidae.
SIZE: up to 36 cm.
DESCRIPTION: a bird with a brown collar splashed with white, the throat and face greyish with a small gold line behind the eye.
HABITAT: dry zones, rocky slopes, open valleys, cultivated areas etc.
COMMENTS: feeds on seeds, fruit and insects.

QUAIL
Coturnix coturnix confisa   Hart

FAMILY: Phasianidae.
SIZE: about 18 cm.
DESCRIPTION: brown bird with a very short tail, the back streaked with black and white, the male has a black patch on the throat.
HABITAT: cultivated areas and pastures.
COMMENTS: feeds on seeds and small insects.

GREY HERON
Ardea cinerea   L.

FAMILY: Ardeidae.
SIZE: up to 90 cm.
DESCRIPTION: back and wings grey, underside white, typically has a black plume behind the eye.
HABITAT: Littoral zone, ponds, pools and reservoirs.
COMMENTS: over-wintering species though some individuals are resident in the Canaries throughout the year. Feeds on small fish and frogs.

WOODCOCK
Scolopax rusticola rusticola   L.

FAMILY: Scolopacidae.
SIZE: up to 34 cm.
DESCRIPTION, the beak is long and straight, the wings rounded at the tip.
HABITAT: laurel   forests   and *Erica/Myrica* woodlands.
COMMENTS: nests on the forest floor, the woodcock is abundant on the island.

RAVEN
Corvus corax tingitanus   Irby

FAMILY: Corvidae.
SIZE: up to 72 cm.
DESCRIPTION: plumage black with a bluish sheen, beak black.
HABITAT: from the coastal zone to the highest point of the island.
COMMENTS: scavenger, noted, in the breeding season, for its acrobatic flight.

LONG-EARED OWL
Asio otus canariensis   Madar.

FAMILY: Strigidae.
SIZE: up to 34 cm.
DESCRIPTION: brown bird, densely black streaked and spotted, the ear tufts long, only visible when the owl is perching.
HABITAT: lower and zones.
COMMENTS: nocturnal, feeds on insects, mainly crickets, small rodents and reptiles.

LIGHT TAILED LAUREL PIGEON
Columba junoniae Hart.

FAMILY: Columbidae.
SIZE: up to 39 cm.
DESCRIPTION: chesnut back with a wine coloured underside. Neck grey with green iridescence.
HABITAT: the Laurisilva.
COMMENTS: a rare and threatened endemic with a limited range.

BOLLE'S LAUREL PIGEON
Columba bollii Godm.

FAMILY: Columbidae.
SIZE: slightly smaller than the white tail, at 38 cm.
DESCRIPTION: robust pigeon with slate grey plumage, green and pink iridescence around the neck.
HABITAT: the Laurisilva.
COMMENTS: rare and threatened endemic.

ROCK DOVE or WILD PIGEON
Columba livia canariensis Bann.

FAMILY: Columbidae.
SIZE: up to 33 cm.
DESCRIPTION: blueish grey with pink and green iridescence around the neck, two black wing bands.
HABITAT: open ground, barrancos, pine forest. The south of the island.
COMMENTS: common, the ancestor of the domestic pigeon.

HOOPOE
Upupa epops pulchra   Floericke

FAMILY: Upupidae
SIZE: up to 27.5 cm.
DESCRIPTION: ochre plumage and a long, slightly curved bill. Large crest displayed in a fan.
HABITAT: open areas from the coast to the mountains.
COMMENTS: insectivorous.

GREY WAGTAIL
Motacilla cinerea canariensis   Hart.

FAMILY: Motacillidae.
SIZE: to 18 cm.
DESCRIPTION: long, characteristic tail, wagged frequently. Grey back, yellow underside and pale feet.
HABITAT: found alongside reservoirs and streams all over the island.
COMMENTS: feeds on insects and small freshwater fish.

BERTHELOTS PIPIT
Anthus berthelotii berthelotii   Bolle

FAMILY: Motacillidae.
SIZE: up to 15 cm.
DESCRIPTION: greyish back and whitish belly. Breast with dark flecks.
HABITAT: slopes and farmland in arid areas.
COMMENTS: feeds on insects and seeds.

BLACKCAP
Sylvia atricapilla obscura   Tschusi

FAMILY: Sylviidae
SIZE: around 14 cm.
DESCRIPTION: black cap above the eyes.
Grey-brown back and light grey breast.
HABITAT: farmland, Laurisilva and fayal-
brezal, barrancos, scrubland.
COMMENTS: common and widespread.

SARDINIAN WARBLER
Sylvia melanocephala leucogastra   (Ledrú)

FAMILY: Sylviidae.
SIZE: up to 13 cm.
DESCRIPTION: black head and white
throat. Eyes ringed with red.
HABITAT: spurge scrubland, farmland,
tamarisk groves, Laurisilva, etc.
COMMENTS: abundant and widespread.

SPECTACLED WARBLER
Sylvia conspicillata orbitalis   (Wah.)

FAMILY: Sylviidae.
SIZE: up to 12 cm.
DESCRIPTION: male has a grey brown
back, dark grey head, pinkish breast and
chestnut wings.
HABITAT: coastal areas, scrub, interme-
diate scrubland and the mountains.
COMMENTS: common and widespread.

CHIFFCHAFF
Phylloscopus collybita canariensis   Hartw.

FAMILY: Sylviidae.
SIZE: up to 11 cm.
DESCRIPTION: brownish green back and cream underside.
HABITAT: all types of vegetation.
COMMENTS: common and widespread

GOLDCREST
Regulus regulus teneriffae   Sebb.

FAMILY: Sylviidae.
SIZE: only 9.5 cm.
DESCRIPTION: male has an orange crest bordered with black. Female crest is yellow, also with a black border.
HABITAT: fayal-brezal, Laurisilva and mixed pine forests.
COMMENTS: common and widespread. Very small.

CORN BUNTING
Emberiza calandra thanneri   Tschusi

FAMILY: Emberizidae.
SIZE: up to 18 cm.
DESCRIPTION: robust beak, back and underside a densely mottled brown.
HABITAT: open ground, pasture land and farms etc.
COMMENTS: common and widespread

CANARY
Serinus canaria L.

FAMILY: Fringillidae.
SIZE: to 12.5 cm.
DESCRIPTION: males have greenish-yellow throat, breast and face. Females duller overall.
HABITAT: farmland, ravines, forests, mountain scrub, etc.
COMMENTS: common and widely distributed

LINNET
Acanthis cannabina meadewaldoi   Hart

FAMILY: Fringillidae.
SIZE: up to 13 cm.
DESCRIPTION: male with the forehead and breast reddish, the back chestnut and the throat with dark brown streaks
HABITAT: shrubby spurge communities, tree heaths, cultivated and dry fields.
COMMENTS:Abundant and widespread.

CHAFFINCH
Fringilla coelebs tintillon W.B. & M.-T.

FAMILY: Fringillidae
SIZE: up to 17 cm.
DESCRIPTION: upper body bluish, forehead black, lower body creamish except the lower abdomen which is white.
HABITAT: forests of all types.
COMMENTS: there are three subspecies in the Canaries.

GOLDFINCH
Carduelis carduelis parva   Tschusi

FAMILY: Fringillidae
SIZE:about 12 cm.
DESCRIPTION: head black, cheeks white, face red, back creamy-brown, tne black wings with a yellow band.
HABITAT: fields, tree heath and degraded laurel forests etc.
COMMENTS: scarce on the island.

ROBIN
Erithacus rubecula microrhynchus   Reich.

FAMILY:Turdidae
SIZE: to 14 cm.
DESCRIPTION: breast and face red or deep orange
HABITAT: laurel forests, tree heath, cultivated zones and ravines.
COMMENTS: common and widely distributed on la Gomera.

CABRERA'S BLACKBIRD
Turdus merula cabrerae   Hart.

FAMILY: Turdidae
SIZE: up to 25 cm.
DESCRIPTION: male jet black with orange-yellow beak, female brown, mottled, beak brown.
HABITAT: in any habitat where there are trees.
COMMENTS: characteristic song.

ROCK SPARROW
Petronia petronia madeirensis   Erlang.

FAMILY: Ploceidae
SIZE: about 15 cm.
DESCRIPTION: earthy-brown colour with blackish markings, the adults with a small yellow patch on the breast.
HABITAT: dry, rocky zones, fields and abandoned buildings.
COMMENTS: local, small populations.

SPANISH SPARROW
Passer hispaniolensis hispaniolensis   (Temm.)

FAMILY: Ploceidae
SIZE: up to 15 cm.
DESCRIPTION: crown and back of the neck dark brown-blackish, cheeks white, breast blackish.
HABITAT: towns, buildings, parks etc.,
COMMENTS: very common and widespread.

BLUE TIT
Parus caeruleus teneriffae   Less.

FAMILY: Paridae
SIZE: about 12 cm.
DESCRIPTION: head very dark blue-black with white markings, back and legs bluish, breast yellow.
HABITAT: forests, fields, ravines, gardens etc.
COMMENTS: locally common, there are 4 subspecies in the Canaries.

RED KITE
Milvus milvus milvus **L.**

FAMILY: Accipitridae
SIZE: up to 66 cm.
DESCRIPTION: chestnut coloured bird of prey with a forked tail.
HABITAT: the highest mountains of the island
COMMENTS: extinct due to the excessive use of DDT in the past to control locust plagues.

OSPREY
Pandion haliaetus **L.**

FAMILY: Pandionidae
SIZE:
Up to 60 cm.
DESCRIPTION: upper parts dark brown, breast white.
HABITAT: coastal cliffs and headlands
COMMENTS: a very rare and threatened species

HOUSE MOUSE
Mus musculus L.

SIZE: up to 13 cm.
HABITAT: from the coast to the highest peaks. Nocturnal and associated with man.
COMMENTS: present on all the islands.

BROWN RAT
Rattus norvegicus L.

SIZE: with tail, up to 50 cm.
HABITAT: lives in extensive burrows. Responsible for spreading disease in the past.
COMMENTS: present on all the islands.

BLACK RAT
Rattus rattus L.

SIZE: up to 48 cm with the tail.
HABITAT: associated with man. Common on boats and around ports.
COMMENTS: originally from Asia. Present on all the islands.

MADEIRAN PIPISTRELLE
Pipistrellus maderensis   Bonaparte

SIZE: small up to 10 cm.
HABITAT: caves and shaded sites.
Nocturnal.
COMMENTS: endemic to the Canaries
and Madeira. Common on La Gomera,
especially in Hermigua and the
Garajonay National Park.

MARINE MAMMALS

COMMON DOLPHIN
Delphinus delphis   L.

SIZE: reaches 2.5 m.
HABITAT: open seas (pelagic).
COMMENTS: often seen swimming in
groups. The most common dolphin in
Canarian waters.

BOTTLE NOSED DOLPHIN
Tursiops truncatus   Montagu

SIZE: larger than the common dolphin,
at up to 2.8 m.
HABITAT: open seas.
COMMENTS: an occasional visitor to
the seas around the islands.

SPERM WHALE
Physeter cotodon   L.

SIZE: reaches lengths of 18 to 20 m.
HABITAT: open sea between the islands.
COMMENTS: feeds on large squid and fish.

PILOT WHALE
Globicephala melaena   Traill

SIZE: up to 8.7 m.
HABITAT: open sea between the islands.
COMMENTS: consumes squid and pelagic fish such as mackerel and "bonito".

KILLER WHALE
Orcinus orca   L.

SIZE: up to 9 m.
HABITAT: open seas.
COMMENTS: an occasional visitor to the area.

GLOSSARY OF TERMS

ACICULAR: needle-like.

AXILLARY: situated in the angle formed by the base of a leaf or the leaf-stalk and the stem.

BATHYLITTORAL: the deepest part of the continental shelf.

BENTHIC: living on the seabed.

BIPINNATE: of leaves, feather-like with the leaflets also divided.

CARAPACE: the hard shell-like back of a crustacean eg. the shell of a crab.

CAPSULE: a simple dry fruit formed by the fusion of two or more carpels.

CILIATED: bearing hairs on the margin

CIRCALITTORAL: open water near the coast.

CLADODE: a branch or stem flattened to simulate a leaf.

CONE: dry fruit of Gymnosperms in which the seeds are protected by woody scales.

CONVOLUTED: coiled or inwardly rolled.

CORYMB: a flat-topped inflorescence with the outer flowers opening first.

CRENULATE: scalloped edge with small, shallow, blunt teeth.

CUNIEFORM: shaped like a wedge.

ENDEMIC: restricted to a particular geographical area.

FASCICLES: condensed, close clusters - fasciculate

FAYAL-BREZAL: low forest vegetation dominated by wax-myrtle and tree heath.

FILIFORM: thread-like

GLABROUS: without hairs

GLAUCOUS: a bluish appearence caused by a whitish surface bloom.

HALOPHILE: salt tolerant, living within the influence of salt spray or brackish water.

HERMAPHRODITE: with male (stamens) and female (ovaries) parts in the same flower.

HISPID: with rough hairs or bristles.

INFLORESCENCE: the flower stem or head of a plant.

INFRALITTORAL: the zone immediately below the low-tide mark.

INTERTIDAL: the area normally exposed between high and low tides.

LANCEOLATE: lance or spear shaped, tapered at both ends with the widest point below the middle.

LARVA: a young immature form, usually morphologically distinct from the adult.

LAURISILVA: dense humid forest dominated by trees of the family Lauraceae.

LIGULE: strap-shaped corolla lobe ("petal") found in the daisy family.

NOCTURNAL: active at night.

OBLANCEOLATE: spear-shaped but broadest above the middle.

OPERCULUM: horny plate on the foot of a snail, used to close the mouth when the animal withdraws into its shell.

ORBICULATE: flat with a circular outline.

OVATE: flat with an egg-shaped outline.

PALMATE: divided in a hand-like manner.

PANICULATE: in the form of a branched, racemose inflorescence.

PELAGIC: living in the open sea.

PETIOLATE: stalked, usually refers to a leaf with a basal stalk.

PINNATE: feather-like.

PINNATISECT: leaves divided in a pinnate way with the lobes cut to the midrib.

PUBESCENT: covered with fine hairs.

RACEME: simple, elongated inflorescence with the oldest flower at the base.

REVOLUTE: leaf-margine rolled downwards with the lower surface innermost.

RUPICOLOUS: living in rocky or cliff habitats.

SINUOUS: with a pronounced wavy margin.

SPATHULATE: spoon-shaped.

SPIKELET: the small floral unit of a grass.

SPUR: long, posterior extension in the form of a tube of the corolla of some plant species such as Kickxia and Viola.

SUBAURICULATE: with short,ear-like extensions at the base of the leaf.

SUPRALITTORAL: the narrow spash-zone immediaiely above the high tide line.

SYMBIOTIC: of two mutually dependent organisms.

TABAIBALES: extensions of shrubby spurge (Euphorbia) vegetation.

THALLUS: the stem of a sea-weed.

THERMOPHILE: warmth loving, open forest of Olea, Pistacia or Juniperus,

TOMENTOSE: densely wooly or pubescent with matted hairs.

TRIFOLIATE: having compound leaves with three leaflets.

UMBEL: a flat-topped inflorescence with the peduncles of more or less equal length and arising from a common point , characteristic inflorescence of the family Umbelliferae.

XEROPHYTIC: living in hot, dry habitats.

BIBLIOGRAPHY

BACALLADO ARANEGA, J.J., ET AL. 1984: *Fauna Marina y Terrestre del Archipiélago Canario*. Edirca S.L. Las Palmas de Gran Canaria.

BARBADILLO ESCRIVA, J.L.., 1987: *La Guía Incafo de los Anfibios y Reptiles de la Península Ibérica, Islas Baleares y Canarias*. Guías Verdes de INCAFO. Incafo S.A., Madrid. 694 pp.

BRAMWELL, D. & BRAMWELL, Z. I., 1983: *Flores Silvestres de las Islas Canarias*. ed. 2. Editorial Rueda, Madrid. 284 pp.

BRAMWELL, D. & BRAMWELL, Z. I., 1987 *Historia Natural de Las Islas Canarias*. Guía Básica. ed. 1. Editorial Rueda, Madrid. 294 pp.

BRITO A., 1991: *Catálogo de los Peces de Las Islas Canarias*. *Editorial Lemus*. Santa Cruz de Tenerife. 230 pp.

DIERL, W., & RING , W., 1992: *Guide des Insects: la description, l'habitat, les moeurs*. ed. 1. Delachaux et Niestlé S.A., Lausanne. Switzerland. En collaboration avec leWWF. 239 pp.

FRANQUET F. & BRITO A., 1995: *Especies de interés pesquero de Canarias*. ed. 1. Gobierno de Canarias. Consejería de Pesca y Transportes. 143 pp.

GARCÍA BECERRA, R., ORTEGA MU—OZ, G., PEREZ SANCHEZ, J.M., 1992: *Insectos de Canarias*. ed. 1. Ediciones del Excmo. Cabildo Insular de Gran Canaria. Departamento de Publicaciones. Las Palmas de Gran Canaria. 418 pp.

GOBIERNO DE CANARIAS, 1985: *Guía de Peces, Crustáceos y Moluscos de interés comercial del Archipiélago Canario*. Consejería de Agricultura y Pesca. 70 pp.

GONZALEZ, N., RODRIGO, J.D. Y SUÁREZ, C., 1986: Flora y Vegetación del Archipiélago Canario. Edirca S.L., Las Palmas de Gran Canaria, 355 pp.

MORENO, J.M., 1988: *Guía de las Aves de las Islas Canarias*. ed. 1. Editorial Insular Canaria S.A. Santa Cruz de Tenerife, 231 pp.

PÉREZ SÁNCHEZ J.M. & MORENO BATET, E., 1991: *Invertebrados Marinos de Canarias*. ed. 1. Ediciones del Excmo. Cabildo Insular de Gran Canaria. Departamento de Publicaciones. Las Palmas de Gran Canaria. 325 pp.

The IUCN Species Survival Commission

1997 IUCN Red List of
Threatened Plants

Edited by Kerry S. Walter and Harriet J. Gillett

Compiled by the
World Conservation Monitoring Centre

IUCN
The World Conservation Union

IUCN RED LIST CATEGORIES

The *1997 IUCN Red List of Threatened Plants is* based on the pre-1994 IUCN Categories, drawn up by the IUCN Species Survival Commission. These have since been revised (IUCN, 1994). Subsequent listings will be made using the 1994 Categories and criteria. Details of both systems are given below.

1994 IUCN Red List Categories

EXTINCT (EX)
A taxon is Extinct when there is no reasonable doubt that the last individual has died.

EXTINCT IN THE WILD (EW)
A taxon is Extinct in the wild when it is known only to survive in cultivation, in captivity or as a naturalised population (or populations) well outside the past range. A taxon is presumed Extinct in the Wild when exhaustive surveys in known and/or expected habitat, at appropriate times (diurnal, seasonal, annual), throughout its historic range have failed to record an individual. Surveys should be over a time frame appropriate to the taxon's life cycle and life form.

CRITICALLY ENDANGERED (CR)
A taxon is Critically Endangered when it is facing an extremely high risk of extinction in the wild in the immediate future.

ENDANGERED (EN)
A taxon is Endangered when it is not Critically Endangered but is facing a very high risk of extinction in the wild in the near future.

VULNERABLE(VU)

A taxon is Vulnerable when it is not Critically Endangered or Endangered but is facing a high risk of extinction in the wild in the medium-term future.

LOWER RISK (LR)

A taxon is Lower Risk when it has been evaluated, does not satisfy the criteria for any of the categories Critically Endangered, Endangered or Vulnerable. Taxa included in the Lower Risk category can be separated into three subcategories:

1. Conservation Dependent (cd). Taxa which are the focus of a continuing taxon-specific or habitat-specific conservation programme targeted towards the taxon in question, the cessation of which would result in the taxon qualifying for one of the threatened categories above within a period of five years.

2. Near Threatened (nt). Taxa which do not qualify for Conservation Dependent, but which are close to qualifying for Vulnerable.

3. Least Concern (lc). Taxa which do not qualify for Conservation Dependent or Near Threatened.

DATA DEFICIENT (DD)

A taxon is Data Deficient when there is inadequate information to make a direct, or indirect, assessment of its risk of extinction based on its distribution and/or population status. A taxon in this category may be well studied, and its biology well known, but appropriate data on abundance and/or distribution are lacking. Data Deficient is therefore not a category of threat or Lower Risk. Listing of taxa in this category indicates that more information is required and acknowledges the possibility that future research will show that threatened classification is appropriate. It is important to make positive use of whatever data are available. In many cases great care should be exercised in choosing between DD and threa-

225

tened status. If the range of a taxon is suspected to be relatively circumscribed, if a considerable period of time has elapsed since the last record of the taxon, threatened status may well be justified.

NOT EVALUATED (NE)
A taxon is Not Evaluated when it is has not yet been assessed against the criteria.

INDEX TO COMMON AND SCIENTIFIC NAMES

227

FAUNA -animals